# Bargain Hunting in the Bay Area

# Bargain Hunting
## in the Bay Area

Second Revised Edition

## by Sally Socolich

**WINGBOW PRESS**

Berkeley

Copyright 1973, 1976 and 1978 by Sally Socolich
ISBN: 0-914728-14-8

**Wingbow Press** books are published and distributed by
**Bookpeople,** 2940 Seventh Street, Berkeley, California 94710

Designed by Hal Hershey, Fifth Street Design Associates
Back cover map by Kirsten Jacobs
Typesetting by Ann Flanagan Typography

REVISED EDITION
First Printing, April 1976
Second Printing, September 1976
Third Printing, April 1977
Fourth Printing, September 1977

SECOND REVISED EDITION
Fifth Printing, July 1978
Sixth Printing, December 1978
Seventh Printing, June 1979

# Contents

See Page 134 for
**Additions and New Listings**

# Introduction

The first two editions of *Bargain Hunting in the Bay Area* were so well received that it was clear readers wanted to know more about where to find good shopping values. Inflationary trends have given birth to a rash of new bargain stores, and others continue to be discovered . . . material for a new volume of *Bargain Hunting in the Bay Area* was everywhere.

This edition of *Bargain Hunting in the Bay Area* leads you in the same direction as previous editions . . . to over 350 stores offering the *best quality goods for the lowest prices*. I have kept my basic bargain criterion of "at least 20% off the retail price," though many entries offer far greater reductions. Many readers of the first two editions have shared their bargain discoveries with me and I have researched and included a number of them.

This book is intended as a guide, of course, and not as an endorsement of the stores listed. Those included are strictly personal selections for which I have accepted no kindnesses or gratuities ot insure their inclusion. To maximize the number of entries for this book I have avoided lengthy descriptions of each store or business, just being wordy enough to reveal its "personality" and spark your interest.

Since store hours are subject to change, I recommend that you call those shops you intend to visit before driving across town. And while addresses and phone numbers were correct at the time of publication, these too are changeable. Subsequent printings will include corrections, and readers are encouraged to notify the author, in care of the publisher, of any such changes.

Please glance over the **Hints for the Bargain Hunter** that follow. You're probably already aware of the basic rules, but the *caveat emptor* rule cannot be over-emphasized. I trust that your innate good shopping habits will caution you to comparison shop before buying and always to ask that number one, all-important question: "How can they sell it so cheap?" I've answered this question in most cases and have tried to lead you to stores that will give you an honest answer. But don't let your guard down—not for a minute! Remember, too, that just because an item is cheap, it's not necessarily a bargain; and to turn the coin over, some merchandise is going to be expensive, even when priced at 20% or more under retail.

I have quoted specific prices in some listings to give you a clue to the kinds of bargains available at the various stores. The prices mentioned are based on research conducted in the late fall of 1977, but because of changes in the economy, those prices may be higher by the time you visit the stores. Still, chances are the ratio of the discount to the retail price will hold.

So, if you're determined to "beat the system," I'm with you. Once you get into the swing of buying at these prices, you'll soon discover that paying straight retail is for the unenlightened—whether for a philodendron or an armoire, a set of encyclopedias, or half a dozen scratch pads. You can buy almost anything at a bargain if you know where to go.

## Hints for the bargain hunter

It's difficult to make specific recommendations about where *you* should shop. Shopping is a highly personal activity and reflects many facets of your personality. Some prefer the tranquil atmosphere of the "better" stores, the sometimes higher quality product and the attentiveness of the personnel that go with it; others are name-brand afficianados and many are just plain budget-conscious. You'll discover that I've listed stores of every possible description; my own personal taste in bargain hunting is quite varied. I shop a chic apparel boutique one day and a bare-bones factory outlet the next. I adore rummaging in salvage and surplus outlets *and* relaxing in an elegant decorator's showroom. Limited facilities, goods, and services don't cause me to blink an eye; my goal is a *bargain*—and hang the tranquility. And if you've bought this book, you probably have one main objective in your shopping ventures: to get the most for your dollar.

## Questions to ask

Whenever an item is for sale to the public at 20-70% under retail, common sense tells you there must be a reason. I have tried in each entry to give you that explanation, and the answer generally falls into one or more of the following categories:

**Loss leader:** An item purposely priced low to get you into the store.

**Discontinued or manufacturer's close-out:** A product that is no longer being manufactured. In most instances this does not affect the merchandise, but where parts may need to be replaced, it could cause a problem.

**In-season buying:** Most retailers buy pre-season, whereas a discounter will often purchase in-season, relieving the manufacturer of merchandise that is old to him but still new to the public.

**Surplus overstocks:** An excess quantity, over and above what is needed by the retailer.

**Overruns:** An excess of products, similar to surplus and overstocks, but generally due to a manufacturer's error.

**Irregulars:** Merchandise with minor imperfections, often barely discernible.

**Seconds:** Merchandise with more than minor flaws which may affect the esthetic appeal or performance of the product.

**Liquidated stock:** When a company or business is in financial trouble, the stock they have on hand is sometimes sold to merchandiser—often by the lot—at prices much lower than retail in order to liquidate the assets of the company.

**Freight damage:** Even if only one or two items in a shipment are broken, burned, chipped, marred, etc., for insurance purposes the entire lot is designated "damaged". This merchandise may be noticeably damaged; often, however, it is actually in A1 condition but part of a shipment that met with physical mishap.

**Sample:** An item shown by the manufacturer's representative to the prospective merchandiser/buyer for the purpose of selling the product.

**Floor sample:** A model displayed in the store.

In addition to the above, the business acumen of one retailer/buyer in purchasing merchandise may be superior to his competitors'; a better original buy generally is reflected in the price. Low overhead can also affect the price; stores in low-rent districts with few frills and little or no advertising can often undersell those in the high-rent areas. The necessity to keep goods moving sometimes forces a retailer into cutting prices—space is a problem in merchandising just as it is in your home . . . they're in it for the long haul, not for the quick profit. Bless them!

Once you have determined the reason the price is low, your next question should be: "Is there anything wrong with the item that will affect its performance or use to me?" Look for flaws before you buy. And if you find one, be realistic about whether you can repair it or have it repaired and still save money. If you've answered all these questions honestly and find the bargain value there . . . plunge, you've bagged a buy. Now you can

relish that delicious feeling of beating the system . . . you've earned it.

## Timing

Many of the shops have specific days that new merchandise comes in. Knowing what those days are will enable you to get the pick of the new crop. When you find a store or outlet that sells merchandise that you're particularly interested in, be sure to ask if they have a mailing list and get on it. This will give you advance notice of sales and new arrivals. For many of these stores, mailing lists are their only form of advertising.

## How to use this book

*Bargain Hunting in the Bay Area* is arranged by categories, very much like the Yellow Pages of your telephone directory. Beneath the subject heading the name of each bargain shop and service is listed in alphabetical order. Also included is such information as address, telephone number, store hours, the means of purchasing, (cash only, cash or check, and which credit cards, if any, are accepted). The credit card code is BA—Bankamericard, MC—MasterCharge, AE—American Express, FN—First National, and VISA. Also listed are the other cities in Northern California where a branch store or similar service is offered.

Because many stores sell a wide variety of merchandise I have not attempted the mammoth job of a complete cross-reference system. I have, however, made a limited number of cross-references where I felt they would be most helpful to the bargain hunter. Please be sure to look at the ''also see's'' when they appear under the main headings. Please consult the index at the end of the book:

**SUBJECT INDEX:** (see page 129)
Arranged by product or service supplied.
**ALPHABETICAL LISTING:** (see page 117)
**GEOGRAPHICAL LISTINGS:** (see page 121)
Arranged by the name of the city in which it is located.

I would be delighted to hear from other bargain hunters regarding new listings for future editions or other suggestions you may have. Please forward any comments to my publisher, **Wingbow Press,** 2940 Seventh St., Berkeley, Calif. 94710.

*Sally Socolich*

## Part One

# Almost All New, Sometimes Irregular, But Otherwise First Class Merchandise

# Appliances

(Also see **Furniture and Accessories—Catalog Discounters, Warehouse Sales; General Merchandise—Catalog Discounters**)

## CVB (CENTRAL VOLUME BUYERS)

1815 So. Monterey Rd. (Betw. Tully & Alma), San Jose. Phone: 998-2906. Hours: M-Sat 10am-6pm, Sun 11am-5pm. Purchases: MC, BA.

Don't be put off by the potholes in the parking lot, the quonset-hut-look of the yellow building or the freight depot appearance of the interior—what really counts are the savings! My price comparisons on name-brand TV's, and kitchen and laundry appliances prove *CVB* fulfills its claims and offers the lowest prices in the area. Most appliances are in the original factory crates, ready for delivery. Others are uncrated for your inspection. *CVB* offers a 30-day trade-in policy, so if you get a lemon (that can happen anywhere) they'll gladly exchange the item for you. Additionally, you have the manufacturer's warranty on all merchandise—double protection. Their 30-day written price-guarantee allows you a refund for the difference if you can find the same merchandise sold elsewhere for less. Now that's laying it on the line! Delivery is nominal: $12.50 from San Jose to Salinas. They take trade-ins on used appliances. Their used appliance department is a real budget saver if you're really broke. Take note—they will not quote prices over the phone.

## CHERIN'S

727 Valencia Street, San Francisco 94110. Phone: 864-2111. Hours: M-F 10am-6pm, Sat 10am-5pm. Purchases: Cash, check. Parking: Street.

A great source for home appliances in every category. This store has a good selection of refrigerators, freezers, washers, dryers, T.V.'s, vacuum cleaners, microwave ovens, VTR's, telephone answering systems, food processors and many other small appliances. Their business is mostly referral. They never advertise their low prices which I found in my comparison shopping to be about the lowest anywhere.

Don't expect them to quote prices over the phone if they don't know you.

## GENERAL ELECTRIC SERVICENTER

1727 No. First Street, San Jose 95112. Phone: 408-298-4126. Hours: M-Sat 8:30am-5:30pm. Purchases: BA,MC. Parking: Private Lot.

One of the very best ways to replace an old or broken General Electric small appliance is through the exchange program offered at the *General Electric Servicenter.* It is possible to trade in that old iron, coffeepot, or toaster oven for another and save approximately 30% off the suggested retail price. On price comparisons I made, the trade-in price was lower than any discount store or catalog discount house.

On display here are reconditioned appliances that carry the following description: "Reconditioned appliances generally represent appliances that have been used in displays or that failed in initial use. They have all been carefully reconditioned by trained GE technicians using new GE replacement parts where required. They have been carefully tested to assure that they meet operating standards required of new appliances and carry the same warranty as new products." On these you can save 30-35%. If what you want isn't on display, be sure to ask—it may be on hand in the storeroom.

## HOUSE OF LOUIE

1045 Bryant St. (near 9th), San Francisco. Phone: 621-1901, 621-7100. Hours: M, Th 10am-9pm; T, F, Sat 10am-6 pm, Sun 1pm-5pm. Purchases: BA, check. Parking: Free lot on side of building.

At this warehouse operation you can get some of the best buys available on appliances and home entertainment needs. Most of the items, such as refrigerators, air conditioners, dishwashers, stoves (including built-ins), stereos, and televisions, are available on a cost-plus 10% basis. You can choose from famous name brands on floor display or from manufacturers' catalogs. On special orders, all sales are final.

Also on display is a wide selection of home furnishings in the low to moderate price range, including chairs, sofas, formal dining room furniture, dinettes, baby furniture, and imported Chinese Modern pieces. Savings are from 20-30%. The better goods can be ordered too, with savings of about 20%. Delivery is free within the city of San Francisco; installation is extra.

## KEN LUFF APPLIANCES

Phone Orders Only: 837-0125. Hours: Recommended calling between 3pm-10pm daily. Purchases: BA, MC.

Many of my Contra Costa friends have purchased their appliances the "lazy way", over the phone. Of course you have to know what you want: brand, name, model numbers, etc. Mr. Luff has the merchandise delivered from the manufacturer's Bay Area distribution warehouse directly to your home. His sources for major appliances include many of the best manufacturers, with all categories of kitchen and laundry appliances. If there's any problem, he'll put you in touch with the manufacturer's authorized repair representative. Doing business this way is unconventional, but I've heard only positive reports from his customers and found my own conversations with Mr. Luff to be not only helpful and informative but very pleasant as well. His prices usually reflect a cost of 10-12% above wholesale.

## NATIONAL SOFA BED AND MATTRESS CO.
(See **Furniture and Accessories**)

## SUNBEAM APPLIANCE SERVICE CO.
655 Mission St., San Francisco 94105. Phone: 362-7195 Hours: M-F 8:30am-5:30pm. Purchases: MC, VISA. Parking: Free Lot.

Other Stores: San Francisco, Santa Clara.

It's not too exciting to have to spend good money on a new iron, mixer, or coffeepot, so bargain hunters will really appreciate the nice selection of "as is" Oster and Sunbeam merchandise available at the *Sunbeam Appliance Service Company.* "As is" items were once display models, salesmen's samples, discounted models, or factory closeouts; all pieces are perfect, both mechanically and electrically, and are guaranteed to perform satisfactorily even when they may have small flaws on the finish or trim. If you have a very old appliance for which there are no longer replacement parts available, you may exchange it for a new model for less than you would pay anywhere else (though colors and models of exchange merchandise are limited). You may also locate some hard-to-find appliances such as egg cookers, large juicers, or meat grinders. They will special-order any new item for you and, of course, can provide or order any Sunbeam or Oster replacement part.

## WESTCLOX FACTORY SERVICE
540 Mission Street, San Francisco. Phone: 777-0560 Hours: M-F 8:15am-5pm. Parking: Pay Lots, Street. Purchases: BA, MC.

Basically a repair center, bargain hunters will want to check carefully their red tag specials always on display. The red tags represent factory reconditioned watches, clocks, and timers that are now fully guaranteed for 90 days. I've seen savings of up to 50% and was particularly impressed with the pile of watches in their glass case. (Many of these are department store returns that failed in initial use.) I was really sorry later, when our electricity blew, that I hadn't picked up one of their red tag travel clocks for $3.99.

# Arts, Crafts and Hobby Supplies

**AKRON** (See **General Merchandise—Discount Stores**)

**AMLING-GILMORE CO.**
(See **Flowers, Plants, Pots**)

**ARTISTS' CO-OPERATIVE OF SAN FRANCISCO**
1750 Union Street, San Francisco 94123. Phone: 885-2052. Hours: Daily 11am-6pm. Purchases: BA, MC, VISA. Parking: Street or Pay Lot.

Artist-owned and artist-operated, the gallery has exhibited the original art of Bay Area painters and sculptors since 1955. The Co-op's founding intention was to provide an exhibiting forum for the areas' new talent and offer the public works of contemporary artists at a reasonable price. Additional savings are possible because the salesman's salary and commission is eliminated by volunteer staffing of member artists. The commission structure differs from privately owned galleries and therefore the artist does not have to price his work as high to receive a fair compensation for his creative efforts. It's possible to purchase works of emerging artists and then find pleasure in watching your art appreciate as subsequent works sell for higher and higher prices.

**CALIFORNIA ART SUPPLY INC.**
3238 Lakeshore Ave., Oakland 94610. Phone: 832-3121. Hours: M-F 9am-5:30pm, Sat 9am-5pm. Purchases: BA, MC, VISA. Parking: Street.

This appealing store advertises discount prices on artists' paints, stretched canvas, selected styles and sizes of frames, plus a complete line of commercial art and graphic supplies. They carry all artists' materials here, so you can plan on a one-stop shopping trip. For quantity purchases of one dozen or more of a certain item, an additional 10% discount is given off the 10-20% already prevailing. Most price tags show both the regular and the reduced price. The salespeople in this store are helpful and well qualified to advise you about your art needs.

**THE CANDLE SHOP**
3020 Middlefield Rd., Redwood City 94063. Phone: 365-7650. Hours: M-Sat 9:30am-5:30pm, Sundays—Nov. and Dec. Purchases: BA, MC. Parking: Street.

Our holidays wouldn't be special if we didn't have candles to mark the occasion. Candles, like everything else, seem to be rather expensive luxuries these days, and that's why *The Candle Shop* is a must on your list of bargain places. This is an outlet for a Peninsula manufacturer, and you'll find a fantastic assortment of just about every kind of candle made in their selection of store returns or seconds. Seconds in candles usually mean that the color wasn't true to the manufacturer standards or they were bruised or chipped in handling. These flaws won't bother you when you compare the prices at *The Candle Shop* to other retail stores. Savings run 50-75% off. A 12″ spiral is just 12¢ compared to 45¢ in a popular brand. You can buy tapers, spirals, novelties, German import, bulk candle wax for your own candle making project along with all the other supplies you may need. There is always a selection of Christmas wreaths and candle holders. This is one place where just a few dollars will go a long way!

## S. DE BELLA BARREL CO.
(See **Building and Do-It-Yourself Materials**)

## FANTASTICO
559 6th Street, San Francisco 94107. Phone: 982-0680. Hours: M-F 6:30am-5:30pm, Sat 8:30am-1pm. Purchases: Cash, check. Parking: Street, Lot.

*Fantastico* is the retail subsidiary of *Angray,* the wholesale supply house for nurseries and florists. Their warehouse has just about everything for all you craft-oriented people. The selection in dried flowers is overwhelming. They stock all those exotic specimens you see in beautiful arrangements in fancy stores, plus all the makings to put them together: tapes, wires, ribbons, foam, etc. My favorite is florist ribbon that I buy in rolls for gift wrapping at ⅓ the cost of the Hallmark types. One roll usually lasts me about a year. For Holiday decorations and ideas, this is the place to come. They also have baskets, plastic flowers and fruits, doll houses, crates, ceramics, terrarium bottles, plant stands and many accessory items. Prices to the general public are usually 20-40% lower than anywhere else. An exception is in their paper and party supply section where retail prices prevail except on quantity purchases.

## FLAX'S WAREHOUSE
1699 Market (corner Valencia), San Francisco 94113. Phone: 391-7400. Hours: M-F 9am-5:30pm, Sat 10am-5pm. Purchases: BA, MC, VISA. Parking: Free Lot.

You don't have to be a starving artist to find the savings and good values at *Flax's Warehouse* appealing. The warehouse operation is notably different from from their downtown store. They've trimmed their operating cost by using a self-service approach: eliminating services like gift certificates, deliveries, store charges etc.; and they've chosen a low rent location.

Basic stocks of leading brands of fine art supplies are discounted 20-50% off the list price. Items like Grumbacher oil colors are 20% off, Bellini oil colors are 30% off, brushes, pastels, water colors, stretched canvas, pre-cut mats, plain and fancy frames, paper and other paraphernalia are discounted appreciably. The selection at this warehouse store is not as complete as their main store. Periodically, closeouts of selected merchandise are displayed with near wholesale prices. Unfortunately, graphic artists won't find much in the selection for their needs.

## NERVO DISTRIBUTORS

650 University Avenue, Berkeley 94710. Phone: 848-6464. Purchases: BA, MC. Hours: T-F, 9am-5pm, Sat 10am-4pm. Parking: Lot.

*Nervo* is a nationwide distributor of stained glass and stained glass supplies. Although most small stores sell scraps, you usually cannot find the selection of scraps or the large scrap pieces that are always on sale at *Nervo*. Discounted catalog items like lamp parts or zinc cane are frequently included in the sale bins. Like all distributors, mistakes occur, goods are damaged, and bargain hunters get the rewards. The business is located directly beneath the University Avenue overpass.

## SAMPLES AND SECONDS ROOM
(See **Giftwares**)

## PATTERNS LTD.

300 Grove St. (behind SF Opera House), San Francisco 94109. Phone: 552-7140. Hours: T-Sun 10am-5pm. Purchases: BA, MC. Parking: Street or Lot.

Great beginnings start here. Long before modern technology, precision wood molds for various ship parts were hand built by craftsmen in a tedious process which is all but lost. Foundry molds today are created from plastics and synthetics and discarded once they have served their purpose. Jacques Terzian, owner of *Patterns Ltd.*, spend his time locating industrial "leftovers" for recycling. Many tables, lamps, and wall pieces are beautifully displayed in his unique store—however, they are not the bargains. The bargains are the assortment of left-overs in the back of his store: old porthole covers, clever as sewing trays; wooden shoe lasts, printers' trays, for nostalgia boxes; old apricot crate panels, perfect for use as garden screens or room dividers; horseshoes right off the feet of thoroughbred horses at Bay Area race tracks. There is no limit to the uses of these materials and you'll find many ideas on their bulletin board which is full of pictures of projects that have been made by his customers. He's happy to have you copy his ideas or to hear about yours.

## ABE SCHUSTER

2940 West St., Oakland 94608. Phone: 653-3588. Hours: M-F 8am-5pm, Sat 9am-4pm. Purchases: BA, MC. Parking: Street.

This warehouse operation, which vibrates with the noise of cutting saws, offers spectacular savings on lucite acrylic sheets for skylights, desk tops, wind breaks, picture frames, furniture, and any other do-it-yourself projects you may have in mind.

You can save 50% off on factory seconds with barely

perceptible flaws. Their regular stock of plastic and plastic-related materials such as plastic letters, corrugated fiberglass, resins, and finishes are priced about 25-40% lower than at other retail stores. They cut sheets to size for a small charge. Green thumbers take note! You can purchase Filon home greenhouse panels for the lowest prices around.

## STANDARD BRANDS PAINT CO.
(See **Building and Do-It-Yourself Materials**)

## SUPER YARN MART
4525 Stevens Creek Blvd., Santa Clara 95050. Phone: 243-2012. Hours: M-Sat 10am-6pm, Sun 10am-5pm. Purchases: BA, MC. Parking: Free lot.

Other stores: Fremont, Hayward.

There are more than 16 branches of this store in the Los Angeles area alone. Their volume buying of carload mill shipments allows them to offer truly fantastic bargains— well, it's almost hard to believe. Lucky Bay Area—we can now save too. The place is a maze of colors; tables piled with yarn here, bins overflowing there, cones hanging neatly on a wall. Whatever kind of yarn you want— cotton, wool, mohair, nylon, or acrylic—you'll find it here. You'll also find novelty yarns, imported and domestic yarns, mill surplus yarns (still on cones), and bulk yarns sold by the pound or ounce. All for sale at reduced

prices, up to 50% off the original retail price. Besides knitting and crochet supplies, they also have all the needlepoint, embroidery, and macrame accessories you could wish for at discount prices. For the less adventurous there are many different kinds of kits (the same ones you see in fancy department stores) for "substantially" less.

## TALLOW TUBBE
1014 Howard, San Mateo 94401. Phone: 347-0554. Hours: M-F 10am-5pm, Sat 10am-4pm except summer. Purchases: Cash, check. Parking: Street.

You'll be greeted by smiling faces at this informal candle shop and factory. Besides taking the seconds, off-colors and overstock from several candle manufacturers, they also make their own. You can catch glimpses of this process going on in the back room. When their own candles come out too long, or too short, or too whatever, they're sold along with the other rejects at 30-40% off. Approximately 80% of the inventory is in the "reject" category. The selection includes tapers, spirals, molded rounds, and decorative candles. Around Christmas time you can buy big blocks of colored candle wax for approximately 20¢ a pound to use in making your own candles or even waxing your water skis.

## UNITED SURPLUS SALES

198 11th St., Oakland 94607. Phone: 893-3467. Hours: M-Sat 9am-6pm. Purchases: BA, MC. Parking: Street, Free lot.

This store is well organized, spacious and airy, with a great variety of things for sale. Twenty percent off retail is offered on all purchases of leading brand-name artists' paints, brushes, and supplies. A large selection of frames is available, including inexpensive unfinished raw oak frames. (A five-day exchange on frames is allowed). Stretched canvas and pre-cut mats are available at the same savings, though there's no exchange or refund on the latter.

Wall-hung rolls of upholstery yardage are sold for 50% off retail with selected seconds occasionally available at even greater savings. All sizes and quantities of foam can be found, and it will be cut to size for you (you'll appreciate this service if you have ever tried to cut a 4-inch slab of foam yourself).

They also sell camping equipment, as well as occasional bargain-priced soft goods (such as clothing, etc.) when they can get it through special purchase.

## LEE WARD'S BARGAIN CENTER

4175 Stevens Creek Blvd., San Jose. Phone: 249-2747. Hours: M-Sat 9am-9pm, Sun 11am-5pm. Purchases: BA, MC. Parking: Lot.

This is the ultimate store for art, craft and hobby supplies. Their every day prices throughout the store are generally a little lower than other craft stores. If you watch their ads in the San Jose ''Mercury'' you can take advantage of their frequent super specials on selected items.

The best buys all the time are in the Bargain Shop, a corner of the store reached only by passing through all the other tempting displays. The Bargain Shop features catalog overstock merchandise which is always first quality and a large assortment of as-is merchandise priced low for fast clearance. There's a brisk turnover in Bargain Shop merchandise which is why people in the area check in frequently. The craft consultants, classes and idea desk are helpful resources for beginners.

# Automobiles and Trucks
## General

### AVIS INC.

200 El Camino, San Bruno 94066. Phone: 877-6763. Hours: M-F 9am-6pm. Purchases: Cash, Certified Check, Financing available. Parking: Lot.

At *Avis* they sell current-model used rental cars that have been completely re-conditioned. They rent and sell primarily General Motors models. Usually cars are deluxe models with air conditioning, power brakes, power steering, and custom accessories. Since *Avis* has already made their money on rental services, you'll find lower prices than in used car lots with comparable models. Inventory changes constantly, so sooner or later they are bound to have the car you have in mind.

## DOLLAR-A-DAY-RENT-A-CAR-SYSTEMS

1815 Old Bayshore Hwy., Burlingame 94010. Phone: 697-5780. Hours: M-F 7am-Midnight. Purchases: Cash, check. Parking: Free lot.

Other Stores: 333 Taylor, S.F.

If you need a compact car, whether foreign or U.S.-made, you can save a lot of money on one here. *Dollar-a-Day* sells their cars after they are rented for 6 months or have 15,000-17,000 miles on them. These are current models whose condition is at least comparable to that of any vehicle you would find at a used car lot. Since *Dollar-a-Day* is not out to sell cars but to dispose of capital equipment, their prices are lower than most lots. The cars are sold between October and March, according to their schedule for replacing rental stock. These cars have all been serviced regularly and are in good to excellent condition. A car will be held for you for several days while you arrange financing. If it takes longer than several days you will be asked for a small deposit, refundable if you change your mind. If you're in the market for a car, you can check on *Avis* and *Dollar-a-Day* at the same time, since they're in the same vicinity.

## HERTZ CAR SALES

300 E. Millbrae Ave., Millbrae 94030. Phone: 877-3737. Hours: M-F 9am-7pm, Sat & Sun 10am-5pm. Purchases: Cash, cashiers check, financing available. Parking: Street, free lot.

Other Stores: Oakland Airport, San Jose Airport.

*Hertz* selects and sells only the finer cars from its rental fleet. Every *Hertz* used car that is offered for sale has a record of service and maintenance that you can check *before you buy. Hertz* backs every car with a Limited Warranty covering the engine, transmission, drive shaft and differential for 12 months or 12,000 miles. All Hertz cars look terrific and are priced to sell. You can expect all the features you're probably looking for: air conditioning, automatic transmission, power steering and brakes, radio and radial tires. Because of their limited driving life, rentals usually have less wear-and-tear on them. They've had more T.L.C. too. There is usually a better selection of cars on Saturdays than any other day of the week. Telephone them for more information. They are very helpful over the phone.

## HIGHWAY PATROL CAR SALE

3601 Telegraph Ave., Oakland. Phone: 658-9111 for information. Hours: Announced. Purchases: Certified or cashier's check only.

Need a good car for towing a boat or house trailer? The *Highway Patrol* retires all their cars when the mileage approaches 75,000 miles, when the performance required for high-speed pursuits may become too demanding Most cars returned for this reason have many years of good use left for the conventional driver. They also have many desirable special features not normally found in used cars, such as heavy-duty equipment for touring or towing, automatic transmissions, air conditioning, and heavy-duty disc brakes. All cars are safety-checked, smog-certified, and compression-checked. They handle beautifully!

When enough cars are accumulated, an auction is held. A minimum bid is placed on each car, along with a description of any mechanical problems that may require attention. Sealed bids are taken and forwarded to Sacramento; holders of winning bids are notified. Some cars are sold in their original black-and-white paint, while others have been painted in bright colors (these cost more). Most cars will be sold for under $1,000 and are usually one to two years old. Look for notices of these sales in the classified section of major newspapers.

## POLICE AUCTIONS
(See **Part II—Auctions**)

# Auto Parts

(Also see **General Merchandise—Catalog Discounters, —Discount Stores**)

## FOUR DAY TIRE STORES
390 East Gish, San Jose 95112. Phone: 293-8323. Hours: W, Th, F, 9am-8pm, Sat 9am-6pm. Purchases: BA, MC.

Other Stores: San Leandro, Sacramento.

*Four Day* has a unique but plausible merchandising approach: they are open only during the most efficient selling hours of the week, which allows them maximum sales with one-shift overhead. Their stock is large, and they say they can fit any type of car (or driver). Their ad in the San Jose ''Mercury'' every week lists practically every cut-price tire they sell; it gives the regular retail price, their credit price, their cash price, their cash and carry price, and the federal excise tax on each tire (as you can imagine, it's a big ad). The brands they sell include Lee (U.S.-made), Bridgestone (Japan), Fulda (Germany), Michelin, Metzeler, and Four Day's own brand. They have their own special guarantee: if one of their tires fails due to workmanship or road hazards or wears out before you have received the guaranteed mileage, you can return the tire and the guarantee and they will give you credit (or mail you cash) for the unused miles (the percentage of unused miles multiplied by the price).

## GRAND AUTO STORES
4240 E. 14th St., Oakland 94600. Phone: 532-1240. Hours: M-Sat 9am-9pm, Sun 8:30am-5pm. Purchases: BA, MC, store charge. Parking: Free lot.

Other Stores: Check phone directory.

For super savings on all your motoring needs—parts, tires, or accessories—you can save up to 70% at *Grand Auto Stores.* They have 62 stores in the Bay Area, so there is probably one close to you. Once my husband sent me into the store with a dirty oily part of our car motor in a paper bag. Not more than a minute after I plunked it onto the counter the salesman had identified it and given me a new one to take home. Needless to say, I was immensely impressed!

Tremendous bargains are offered every day on items such as name-brand American-made batteries, spark plugs, motor oil, oil filters, and tires. Follow the ads every week in your major newspapers; if you live within their catalog distribution area, you can check for additional great buys not included in their newspaper ads.

*Grand Auto* also carries fishing, camping, and gardening equipment, bicycles and a wide selection of toys at Christmas. (For one week after Christmas all toys are reduced 50% off their regular price).

A special bargain at *Grand Auto* are blemished tires, which are mechanically sound and give the same service as a first-quality tire. Most of the stores also have repair and service centers staffed with licensed mechanics.

## SCHERBA'S

1497 El Camino Real, Millbrae 94030. Phone: 589-4545. Hours: M-F 9am-9pm, Sat 9am-5:45pm, Sun 9:15-5pm. Purchases: BA, MC. Parking: Street, Free lot.

Other Stores: Palo Alto, Redwood City, San Francisco, San Mateo, South San Francisco.

According to a lot of men I know, *Scherba's* is one of the best places to save a buck or two on car parts and accessories. You will be overwhelmed at their complete selection and low prices—10-30% on many items. Check their ads in your local newspaper for special sales, when you can usually save even more. The salespeople here are generally knowledgeable and helpful.

# Books and Magazines

You don't have to look very long or very far to find bargains in books. Most book stores in the Bay Area feature bargain tables or sections all the time. For this reason I'm not listing any stores individually.

The selections on these bargains tables usually fall in the category of publishers' closeouts, remainders, out-of-print, or damaged books. One of the best times to add to your home library is in January and February. Most stores have special sales to reduce their inventory before taxes. You can even find very new and current best sellers at discount prices.

A quick glance through the yellow pages in your phone book will reveal the many stores specializing in used books and magazines, some with issues going back 30-50 years.

Of course, don't overlook your local Book Fair that is held by many libraries and fund raising organizations. I've had very good luck buying children's books this way, as long as I arrive on the scene the moment the sale starts.

## FEDERAL BOOKSTORE

Federal Building, 450 Golden Gate Ave., San Francisco 94102. Phone: 556-6657. Hours: M-F 8am-4pm. Purchases: Cash, check. Parking: Street (limited).

The *U.S. Government Printing Office* publishes thousands of pamphlets and books on a variety of topics of interest to the average and not-so-average person (judging by the subjects). The information contained in these publications has been researched by the U.S. Government, and comes to you at real bargain prices not much over actual printing cost. Prices start at 15¢-25¢.

The variety of topics is endless: home economics, baby and child care, civil defense, income tax, budgeting, education, agriculture, language, law enforcement, drugs, Social Security, Geological Survey maps, and the Congressional Record (if you want to wade through it). These are just a few of the subject areas. You can call and request a list of pamphlets on particular topics (one of those mentioned above or one of your own choosing), and they will gladly oblige. They fill mail orders too.

Try to visit the store and check over the many publications available. Parking near the Federal Building is difficult. Good luck!

# Building and Do-It-Yourself Materials

(Also see **General Merchandise—Liquidators; Part II: Surplus Stores; Wrecking and Salvage Yards**)

## General

**BEST BLOCKS, INC.**
34840 Alvarado-Niles Rd., Union City 94587. Phone: 471-1966. Hours: M-F 7:30am-5pm, Sat 8am-4pm. Purchases: BA, MC, VISA.

It's really not necessary to rip-off construction sites for building blocks because at this manufacturer's yard there are blocks for everything from hi-rise buildings to back yard barbecues. Best of all, there is always a selection of seconds and off-color blocks at savings of 15-50%. On their top quality overstock blocks you can save by buying directly from the source and on quantity purchases you can save an additional 15%. You can choose from slump blocks, stepping stones, patio tile (including seconds), garden blocks, tree rings and decorative rock. They have over 600 sizes, styles and shapes. Whether you're building a tile patio, or installing your own fireplace, they can tell you how to do it, what you will need, and what it will cost. Delivery service available at reasonable charge; technical and design literature available at no cost. All you need is the muscle to do the job!

## S. DE BELLA BARREL CO.
1176 Harrison St., San Francisco 94103. Phone: 861-1700. Hours: M-F 8am-4pm. Purchases: Cash, check. Parking: Street.

Salvatore De Bella is one of the biggest importers and manufacturers of barrels in the nation. His barrel factory is a perfect setting for a shoot-it-out scene from one of the popular TV detective series (I was ready to take cover as soon as I heard a shot). There are mountains of barrels, about 3,000 of them, stacked 30 feet high. When you come in you may see the coopers (barrelmakers) at their noisy work; I was fascinated by their skill and precision.

The imported used barrels may have held Irish whiskey, French cognac, Kentucky bourbon, or West Indian rum. The barrels are cleaned and restored for use as planters, tables, stools, cradles, dog houses or what have you. Best of all, a used 60-gallon barrel sells for only $15.00, a half barrel for only $7.50. Spigots and barrel stands are also available. If your taste runs to the exotic, you may be interested in the handmade handcarved oval oak barrels, a *De Bella* specialty.

## NISSAN TILE
697 Veterans Blvd., Redwood City. Phone: 364-6547. Hours: M-Sat 8am-5pm, Sat 9am-4:30pm. Purchases: BA, MC, VISA. Parking: Street.

You can't possibly imagine the potential for beauty, design and interest in your home until you contemplate the selection of tile at *Nissan*. Their showroom floor is a patchwork of exotic and different tile patterns; in fact I could hardly bring myself to walk across. Nissan claims they are the

biggest importer of ceramic tile in the Bay Area . They distribute to tile contractors and retail stores. They have Italian, Japanese and Domestic tiles. You can save 30% on tile sold under the *Nissan* label and on odd lots left over from custom jobs. They have supplies for do-it-yourselfers and all the free advice you need.

## STANDARD BRANDS PAINT CO.
2233 Contra Costa Blvd., Pleasant Hill 94523. Phone: 686-2413. Hours: M-F 8am-9pm, Sat 8am-6:30pm, Sun 9am-5:30pm. Purchases: Cash, check. Parking: Free lot.

Other Stores: Colma, Daly City, El Cerrito, Hayward, Mountain View, Oakland, San Jose, San Mateo, San Rafael.

Paint is the basis of *Standard Brand's* good name. They sell endless varieties of it, as well as other hardware and decorator items for the home. The discounts are 10-50% off retail prices and their products are good. Grab a shopping cart and browse around. When you need assistance, go to the center of the store and take a numbered ticket. Their salesmen give expert advice and service.

There are two prices on every tag. The crossed-out figure indicates the retail price for comparable quality; the second price is your cost. You save the difference.

Here's a sample listing of their merchandise: paints and accessories of all kinds, ladders, floor and carpet tiles, wallpaper, shutters, ceramic tiles, plastic beads, art supplies, picture frames and glass, candlemaking equipment, casting resin, and some 8,000 other items in all departments.

Our family has used *Standard Brands'* products for many years.

# Tools

## BLACK AND DECKER MANUFACTURING CO.
15206 E. 14th, San Leandro. Phone: 276-1610. Hours: M-F 8am-5pm, Sat 9am-1pm. Purchases: MC, BA, VISA. Parking: Street.

Other Stores: Santa Clara, South San Francisco.

If your husband is a "Handy Andy" and loves to buy new tools for his own garage workshop, make sure he checks *Black and Decker* before investing any money in tools. The reason is simple: there are many "reconditioned" tools available here at great savings, such as sanders, saws, drills, even lawn edgers and lawn mowers. These reconditioned tools may have been returned by their owner within 90 days because of performance failures. They have had a trip back to the factory and are now provided with all new parts and the same one-year guarantee as new tools. Some other tools are box-damaged or were once salesmen's samples.

The savings range from 20-35% off regular retail. Because the supply and availability of these tools may vary, you should call them about what you want; they will gladly take your name and notify you when your tool is available.

## ROCKWELL POWER TOOL CENTER
3039 Teagarden Street, San Leandro, 94577. Phone: 357-9762. Hours: M-F 8am-4pm. Purchases: BA, MC.

They operate in a similar fashion to *Black & Decker* and *Skil Power.* If you're a *Rockwell* man, you'll appreciate the price reductions on their reconditioned power tools especially during sale times when savings can approach 50% off retail prices.

## SKIL POWER TOOL SERVICE CENTER
425 Jackson St., Oakland 94607. Phone: 444-1559. Hours: M-F 8am-5pm. Purchases: BA, MC. Parking: Street, free lot.

Other Stores: Santa Clara, Brisbane.

If you have a broken electric home shop tool, you're lucky if it's made by *Skil Power Tools,* for you can probably trade it in for a new one if reconditioning is too expensive. On a trade-in you save about 30% on the less expensive and up to 50% on the more expensive tools. (Not every tool in the Skil line is included in their exchange program, however.)

There are three categories of tools available with savings up to 25%. All are specifically labeled with special tags which state: "To assure the controlled high quality required for sale at a Skil Service Center, Rebuilt Power Tools, Discontinued Models, and Factory Appearance Rejects are tested for conformance to original equipment standards. Factory Trained Repair Technicians have performed a complete Detectron diagnostic examination of the tool. All repairs and/or parts replacement have been made as required to effect a like-new operative condition. Each of these tools is guaranteed against defects caused by faulty materials or workmanship." These tools carry the same guarantee as their other retail tools.

The Skil line includes lawn edgers, sanders, drills, jig saws, hand saws, and Recipro saws. Occasionally they have discontinued industrial tools. They will gladly try to locate a reconditioned tool at one of their other service centers for you if what you want is not on display. You can call in advance for information on the availability of a special tool.

# Cameras

(Also see **General Merchandise—Catalog Discounters, Discount Stores**)

## SAN JOSE CAMERA

25 W. San Fernando Street, San Jose 95113. Phone: (408) 295-8591. Hours: Mon-Sat 9am-5:30pm. Purchases: BA, MC.

Photo-buffs who are interested in the more sophisticated, exotic and usually more expensive cameras and accessories will feel right at home in this tiny camera shop. Most major brands are carried: Leica, Cannon, Nikon, Olympus, Vivitar, Rollei, Minolta, Pentax, Hasselblad, and Mamiya.

I would suggest that you do some research regarding your needs and selections before coming here because their staff is limited and they're usually very busy. They simply don't have the time to give you lengthy demonstrations or sales talks. If you can tell them what you want, they'll probably be able to give you the lowest price in the

Bay Area. They are very good about standing behind their merchandise or handling any problems.

# Carpets and Floor Coverings

(Also see **Furniture—Catalog Discounters, Liquidators**)

Comparison shopping is essential when bargain hunting for carpeting and other floor covering. Some stores give you a lower price on the carpet but make up for it with their installation and padding costs, while others charge a slightly higher price for the carpeting but toss in the installation and padding for free. The variance in price is the only constant. Always remember to price the carpet and padding separately, since there are different weights and quality to consider in padding. When comparing the total cost among the stores, be sure you're comparing the same quality carpeting, padding, and installation. Ask how they plan to arrange the carpet seams and how they will be joined. Ask also what kind of stripping will be used when soft and hardcover floor coverings meet. Be sure to tell the salesman what you expect of the carpet (how long you expect it to last, the kind of traffic it will bear, its exposure to strong sunlight, etc.). He will be better able to advise you.

The cunning and expertise of the retail carpet store buyer will greatly affect the price you pay. One carpet store may pull a coup in a big buy, enabling them to sell that stock at a lower price than its competitors. Two months later a different store may make the best buy, and then sell at a lower price. Carpet "wholesalers" abound throughout the Bay Area, and they are able to offer good buys because of their different business styles. Some stores specialize in buying overstocks and closeout patterns and colors. Others buy room-size remnants or pieces in off-color dye lots. Some specialize in bankrupt stocks. For these many reasons you can save on your carpeting dollar. Remember that it's a changing market. Always take your time, comparison shop, and consider all factors.

## CARPET TOWN WAREHOUSE STORES

877 E. Hamilton Ave., Campbell 95008. Phone: 371-3323. Hours: M-F 9am-9pm, Sat 9am-6pm, Sun 11am-5pm. Purchases: BA, MC, FN. Parking: free lot.

Other Stores: Mountain View.

*Carpet Town* has so many pieces of beautiful carpet to choose from that it is difficult to make a selection. Sometimes the pieces are stacked so high it's hard to see them—but rest assured that what you want is undoubtedly in there somewhere waiting for you to dig it out. Make your choice from what's there—no special orders are taken. You can select for either a room or your entire house. If you need a small piece, check out their remnants, which are especially excellent buys (they've marked them for size to make it easy for you). Each piece has a tag with the regular price and *Carpet Town's* price on it. The salesmen here are

quite accomodating; if you decide on a carpet or want to choose something at home, a man will come out to measure your floor space or being samples. *Carpet Town* can also lay your carpet, at regular retail labor costs.

## LAWRENCE CONTRACT FURNISHERS.

470-B Vandell Way, Campbell 95008. Phone: (408) 374-7590 Purchases: Cash, check. Hours: M-F 8am-5:30pm. Parking: Lot.

For South Bay shoppers *Lawrence's* is one of the best resources for carpeting, vinyl floor coverings, hard wood flooring kits, draperies, wallpapers and many fine furniture lines. The showroom is small, mostly stocked with wallpaper books, carpet and flooring samples. It's almost too much to take in all at once. Installation of flooring and carpeting will be provided (of course you pay for it) but I've found their prices to be lower than most other places. They can't provide decorator services at these prices, but they enjoy a reliable reputation. To find this out-of-the-way showroom from the San Tomas Expressway, take the Winchester offramp in Campbell, go West to Hacienda, turn left, and turn right on Dell. Lawrence is on the corner of Vandell and Dell.

## S & G DISCOUNT OUTLET

505 S. Market St., San Jose 95113. Phone: 292-8971. Hours: M-W, F, Sat 9am-5pm; Th 9am-9pm. Purchases: BA, MC. Parking: Free lot.

One of the largest selections of linoleum I have ever seen, for 10-30% less than regular retail, *S & G* carries Armstrong, Congoleum, Ozite, and other brands of floor coverings.

Indoor-outdoor carpeting is also for sale at a savings. S & G supplies to the trade, and the pace is sometimes pretty busy. When you go, know what you want and have with you the measurements of the floor you want covered (for one thing, you might find just what you need among their remnants). They had a fairly large selection when I was there, but turnover is brisk.

## TRADEWAY STORES WAREHOUSE
350 Carlson Blvd. (next to Blue Chip Stamp Redemption Center), Richmond 94804. Phone: 233-0841. Hours: M-Sat 10am-5:30pm, Sun noon-5pm. Purchases: BA, MC. Parking: Free lot.

Other Stores: El Cerrito.

If you're looking for bargain prices on carpeting, this warehouse for the *Tradeway Stores* offers a tremendous selection of carpeting that has been written off as an insurance loss. Name-brand carpet mills also dispose of overruns, excess inventories, seconds, and off-color carpeting here. You will feel as if you're walking on the bottom of the Grand Canyon—carpeting is stacked in rolls 20 feet high, and higher. If you want to see a particular piece, a man will get it for you with a special forklift.

Savings are usually about 30% though on unusual or novelty carpeting you may save as much as 70-80%. This is strictly a case of "what you see is what you get." There are no special or custom orders, but it is unlikely that what you want won't be there in their huge inventory. Padding is sometimes available at below wholesale prices. They do not install, but will refer you to installers. All carpet on display is conveniently ready for immediate delivery, though

you will save additional money if you take the carpet home yourself, or have your installer pick it up.

Not to be overlooked are the second and third floors of this warehouse. They are jammed, piled, and stacked with distressed furniture, also representing manufacturers' fire and insurance losses. On some pieces you can actually see where the flames left their mark, although this is unusual. Many well-known manufacturers are represented in this tremendous selection of furniture for any room in the house at savings of as much as 40%. Delivery is free on large pieces, although your price will be reduced it you carry it off by yourself. All sales are final.

# Christmas Decorations

(Also see **Arts, Crafts and Hobby Supplies**)

## DISPLAY DIMENSIONS
1169 Mission Street, San Francisco 94102. Phone: 861-6300. Hours: M-Sat 10am-5pm *Month of November*. Purchases: Cash, check. Parking: Street.

Every year for one month *Display Dimensions* opens its' doors to the public. Those elegant and clever decorations, fixtures and accessories you see in store displays are often designed and sold by this outfit. How often have you seen just the right thing and then been told that it was not for sale but for display only?

During their month-long sale you can buy Xmas decorations, ornaments, seasonal decorations, garment racks, fixture hardware, baskets, trim items, home furnishings items, one-of-a-kind designs and decorative accessories. All merchandise is priced slightly above their cost. This is not the place to take children! I usually lose myself in contemplation of all the treasures for at least an hour before making my selections. *Display Dimensions* is also an excellent resource for small stores with a limited decorating budget.

# Clothing
## Children's Clothing

**BABY WONDERLAND**
(See **Furniture and Accessories—Baby Furniture**)

**CAPWELL'S BUDGET STORE**
(See **Women's Clothing**)

**CLOTHES CIRCUIT**
(See **Women's Clothing**)

**THE ELEGANT STORK**
132 So. First, San Jose. Phone: 279-1920. Hours: M-Sat 10am-6pm. Purchases: BA, MC. Parking: Lot, Validated behind store.

Everyone who flinches at the prospect of outfitting the latest family addition will be relieved to see the selection and great prices on infant furniture, accessories and infant and toddler clothing. Savings range from 25-50%.

The owners of this shop buy salesmen's samples of some of the best known nationally advertised clothing lines. Sizes range from 3mos to 6X. You can expect to find diaper sets, dresses, mix and match sets, suits, coats, etc. Many are one of a kind. The labels are cut on some really expensive brands but you can recognize the quality.

The baby furniture is acquired from manufacturers' closeouts, department store display pieces which may have been damaged, and samples. They repair any defects and then guarantee the merchandise. They also have a replacement parts inventory for customers who wish to do their own repairs. All merchandise is guaranteed to be safe and in accordance with federal safety standards.

You can pick up these bargains on weekends at the *San Jose Flea Market,* where *The Elegant Stork* has a stall.

## GABARDINE'S
(See **Family Clothing**)

## JAMBOREE
5630 Geary, (Betw. 20th & 21st Ave.). San Francisco 94121. Phone: 751-9000. Hours: M-S 9:30-6pm, Sun 12am-5pm. Purchases: BA, MC, VISA. Parking: Street, City Lot.

Other Stores: Sunnyvale, Walnut Creek

If you like to see your children turned out in style but you can't cope with high prices, *Jamboree* is the place. A little paint and good taste goes a long way in making a discount operation look like a fashionable childrens shop. Most impressive are the European and American designer labels on the clothing as well as the most desirable and appreciated better American brands. Savings range from 20-50% off retail prices. These are not seconds or irregulars or out-of-season clothes. The stock is plentiful! I'm always thrilled when I find fancy dress clothes for my children at double reduced clearance prices. When you know you'll give something away or pass it along before it shows signs of wear, the savings is appreciated even more.

Size ranges from infants through 14 in boys and girls clothing. Exchanges are allowed but no cash refunds. No children of your own? Give one of their gift certificates!!

## MARSHALL'S
(See **Family Clothing**)

## STORK TOWN
(See **Furniture and Accessories—Baby Furniture**)

## THE TREEHOUSE
1815D Ygnacio Valley Blvd., Ygnacio Plaza, Walnut Creek 94596. Phone: 935-0827. Hours: M-Sat 10am-5:30pm. Purchases: BA, MC. Parking: Lot.

Other Stores: 310 Linda Lane, Danville.

The ladies who own this store spend a lot of time dealing with sales representatives, buying sample merchandise for their charming children's shop. The samples in boys' and girls' clothing, from the best manufacturers, come in infant sizes through size 14. They also have nightgowns, bathrobes, Communion dresses, Baptism outfits, playclothes and gorgeous dress ensembles for the little ones' special occasions. Savings range from 25-33% off except during sales when reductions are greater.

# Family Clothing

(Also see **Men's** and **Women's Clothing**)

## CAPWELL'S BUDGET STORE
Broadway at 20th St., Oakland 94612. Phone: 832-1111. Hours: M, Th, F 9:30am-9pm; T, W, Sat 9:30am-6pm. Purchases: Cash, check, store charge. Parking: Street, pay lot.

A fun way to get to *Capwell's Budget Store* is to ride BART to the 19th Street Station, where you will exit directly into the store below street level. You'll find almost everything here but furniture, stationary supplies, home appliances, and decorator items. Your incentive for shopping here is high fashion at low prices; at the *Budget Store* you can buy today's "in" look at a fraction of the price you'd pay upstairs.

Special purchases of selected irregulars, samples, and seconds are made from name-brand manufacturers in men's, ladies' and children's clothing. Labels are sometimes removed or stamped "irregular," but the experienced shopper will recognize the popular manufacturers. The linen and bedding department has a January White Sale going on all year long, and the yardage department offers super bargains on remnants and savings on an assortment of first-quality fabrics.

All regular store services are available in the *Budget Store*. Ads spotlighting special bargains appear three times a week in the Oakland "Tribune."

## CLOTHES CIRCUIT
(See **Women's Clothing**)

## EMPORIUM BASEMENT STORE
(See **Linens**)

## GABARDINE'S FAMILY DISCOUNT STORE
3357 E. 14th St., Oakland 94601. Phone: 532-7273. Hours: M-Th, Sat 9:30am-5:45pm; Fri 9:30am-8:45pm; Sun 11am; 4:45pm. Purchases: BA, MC, store charge. Parking: Street, pay lot.

Other stores: San Pablo.

Just about every style of clothing for every occasion awaits you at this neat but not fancy store, a bargain resource for the discriminating shopper. In the ladies', children's, and men's departments there are many closeouts, irregulars, and manufacturers' samples from name-brand companies, 40-50% off.

Regular merchandise is available at regular prices to supplement the special merchandise and to insure a constant selection. There is also a small shoe department that offers good savings on stylish shoes for the family. There are dressing rooms and other department store services such as a layaway plan.

## MARSHALL'S
5160 Stevens Creek Blvd. (at Law. Expy), San Jose 95129. Phone: 408-244-8962. Hours: M-S 9am-10pm, Sun Noon-5pm. Purchases: BA, MC. Parking: Free Lot.

At *Marshall's,* it's department store selection (minus

atmosphere) with many brand names selling for less than retail. Their clothing departments for men, boys, girls, infants and women are the largest part of *Marshall's* inventory. Their shoe department has excellent buys and low and behold, they even have a lingerie and robe department. 20-60% savings are offered on merchandise categorized as irregular, samples or overruns. Some labels are cut. *Marshall's* has a full money back refund policy within 14 days of purchase with a sales slip verification. That's nice! Not to be overlooked are the linen, housewares, and gift departments where you can purchase sheets, spreads, and dust ruffles etc., at prices that should make white sale ad-makers blush. Conveniently *Macy's Furniture Clearance Place* is next door—two great bargain places side by side.

## MONTGOMERY WARD CLEARANCE CENTERS
(See **General Merchandise—Liquidators**)

# Men's Clothing

(Also see **Family, Women's Clothing**)

## BELMONT CLOTHES
915 Ralston Ave., Suite B, Belmont 94002. Phone: 591-8760. Hours: M-F 10am-5:30pm, Sat 10am-5pm. Purchases: BA, MC. Parking: Private lot, street.

Professional and career men who are interested in dependable, enduring fashion rather than the latest fads and trends will be impressed with the fine quality and modest prices at *Belmont Clothes.* Discreetly tucked away behind a bank, the store is immaculate and simply furnished with most available space taken up by racks of suits, sportcoats, and slacks. In fact, they only sell these three items. Each item has a letter code on the hang tag which you compare to their posted price list which reflects their reduced prices compared to a suggested retail price. Rather than the 60-70% mark-up of other men's retailers, the owners of this store take a 30% mark-up. With lower overhead, minimal advertising expenses, they still make a respectable profit and their customers reap a tidy savings!

Suits range in price from $96-$189, sportscoats, $69-$139, and slacks, $15-33. Most of the selection is obtained from well known American manufacturers although they do stock imported merchandise too. Their selection is very extensive in all three categories with hard to find sizes available in good quantities. At these prices it's understandable that they charge extra for alterations. Once you get on their mailing list you'll be kept informed of their latest shipments and special sales. Finally, their low-key, no pressure approach to selling is very refreshing and most appreciated.

## CASA SPINALI

375 Sutter (7th floor), San Francisco 94108. Phone: 397-9205. Hours: M-Sat 9am-6pm. Parking: Street.

Men's suits are hung on 4 tiers on both sides of this store. For slacks, blazers, sportcoats and fine suits this is an excellent resource. With the lower overhead, *Casa di Spinali* can sell American and imported brands with a 30% mark-up instead of the usual 60-70% markup and still make a profit. I found their silk ties at $4.88 a super buy.

You'll have to add the cost of alterations to the price, which they do very reasonably. A professional man can easily find a beautiful suit for approximately $129.00 that would cost considerably more at other downtown stores. Their low prices make it hard to keep their Ultra-suede and leather jackets in stock.

For women who love all those famous labels seen advertised in Vogue and Harpers Bazaar, their accessories sport those status designer initials and logos on handbags, totes, scarves, etc. Savings on these accessory lines are substantial compared to the prices at other posh stores around Union Square. In addition, they carry designer and better brand blouses, ladies' suits (many suede and Ultra-suede), leather boots, sweaters, shearlings and pants.

## DAVID'S SHIRTS AND SWEATERS

649 Laurel Street, San Carlos 94070. Phone: 592-6377. Hours: M-Sat 10am-5:30pm. Purchases: BA, MC. Parking: Street.

There are so few resources for men that although this store offers modest 10-20% discounts it should not be overlooked. The best buys are on cardigan, turtleneck or pullover sweaters.

Sports shirts in casual to conservative styles are usually discounted 10-20% and there is a good selection of name brand casual pants. There are better discounts (up to 40% off) when they have a sale. Get on their mailing list!

## EMPORIUM BASEMENT STORE
(See **Linens**)

## EXECUTIVE CLOTHES
520 Washington St., San Francisco 94111. Phone: 433-7818. Hours: M-F 9:30am-5:30pm, Sat 10am-3pm. Purchases: MC, BA, VISA. Parking: Street or Pay Lot.

You're greeted at this store across from the Transamerica Building by a loud jarring buzzer as you open the gate into the sales area. After you've calmed your pounding heart and nerves you can start to appreciate the selection of men's suits, sportcoats, slacks, shirts and ties. All the merchandise sports their private label making comparison shopping difficult. (I find this impediment very common in the area of men's clothing.) However, if you're familiar with the merchandise sold in other retail stores you will recognize at *Executive Clothes,* the same quality and fine tailoring, but at a much lower price. Their selection of three piece wool suits in the $140.00 price range is extensive, and the stylish camel hair sportscoats at $129.00 were excellent values.

Most of their merchandise is purchased from American manufacturers whose styles are designed for the professional or executive mien. They maintain a complete size range which includes many hard to find sizes. Alterations are extra, but they will have them done for you at a very reasonable cost.

## HALL'S CLOTHING
7410 Monterey Hwy, Gilroy 95020. Phone: 842-2015. Hours: M-Sat 9am-6pm, F 9pm-8pm. Purchases: BA, MC, VISA. Parking: Street.

Stacks and stacks of name-brand jeans, denims, and cords are found in this small but well-established outfitter for Western clothes. First quality pants sell for discount prices. Their stock of second-quality is discounted 30-40% but selection depends on availability. The flaws are slight. Be sure to ask for your size. The back room is filled with additional stock.

## KORET OF CALIFORNIA
(See **Women's Clothing**)

## MARSHALL'S
(See **Family Clothing**)

## MEN'S SHIRT AND SWEATER OUTLET
8200 Capwell Drive, Oakland. Phone 635-8400. Hours: M-Th 11am-2:30pm, F 11am-4pm. Purchases: Cash, check, Parking: Free lot.

A pleasing selection of men's ski sweaters, mod T-shirts, golf shirts, and sports shirts is available at this manufacturer's outlet for a well-known brand found in better men's stores and department stores.

Finding the outlet takes all your investigative skills, since it is obscurely located at the side back corner of the building. A small hand-lettered sign saying "Open" is the only indication of the treasure trove of men's wear within. Merchandise is neatly arranged on tables or racks. There are dressing rooms. Exchanges are permitted, but no cash refunds or credit slips.

## MERCHANDISERS, INC.

200 Folsom St., San Francisco 94105. Phone: 543-2232. Hours: M-F 8am-5pm. Purchases: Cash, check. Parking: Street.

This business grew like topsy from a wholesale distributor who opened an outlet to accommodate his friends to what is now a successful retail operation that can accommodate just about any sportsminded man. It's very accessible to the businessman in the financial district who makes this a regular lunchtime outing. Except for the Christmas season, they're closed Saturday and Sunday and evenings, which definitely limits the shopping of patrons from outside the area.

There is an impressive selection of name-brand sportswear—Izod shirts, Munsingware, Glen Oak slacks, Leader of Calif., Paris and Hickok belts, Allen Edwards shoes, to name just a few. They also carry golf and tennis equipment and clothing, and a nice selection of jogging suits. Everything is marked on a cost plus basis, which is considerably less than the markup of full service stores. Savings range from 30-45% on almost all merchandise.

## PANTS O/OFF

2279 Taylor Street, San Francisco 94122. Phone: 775-2522. Hours: M-F 10am-9pm, Sat 10am-6pm, Sun 12pm-5pm. Purchases: BA, MC, VISA. Parking: Free Lots.

Other Stores: Concord, Cupertino, Daly City, Palo Alto, Petaluma, San Jose.

This is a specialty discount store that carries famous brands at super savings. *Pants O/Off* also acts as a clearance outlet for GAP retail pants stores. Signs posted in the stores tell you clearly what is available: 1) first quality closeouts, 2) products by Levi Strauss & Co., 3) some slightly irregular merchandise. Price tickets are color coded with most prices ranging from $4.99 to $9.99. Savings range from 15%-75% on the merchandise and even more extraordinary bargains prevail on the sale racks. There is a great selection of guy's and gal's casual pants, tops, and jackets in a full range of sizes.

Unlike many other outlets these stores are clean and nicely decorated with bold colored signs. There's plenty of merchandise, displayed as neatly as in better department stores and there are several private dressing rooms.

# Women's Clothing

(Also see **Family Clothing**)

With 54 separate listings for women's clothing I have tried to divide the listings into three categories so the shopper can more easily determine the type of business involved.

*Factory Outlets:* Stores owned and operated by a clothing manufacturer, usually located on or near the manufacturers plant. Most of these stores elect to keep a low profile, and depend on word of mouth advertising. Most prefer to go nameless or choose an innocuous name like Factory Outlet or Factory Store which makes it difficult sometimes to figure out who they really are and what labels they sell. Factory outlets rarely take credit cards and may have unconventional hours.

*Retail Bargain Stores:* The stores in this section are privately owned, even though many use the term "factory" or "outlet" in their name. The bargains and savings at these stores can be as substantial as at the factory outlets. Also, they have a greater diversity in fashion selection since, in addition to fashion from local manufacturers, they offer fashions from manufacturers around the country. These stores sell overruns, samples, close-outs, and factory irregulars. They usually take advantage of in-season buying (larger retail stores place their orders far in advance of the season), relieving the manufacturer of merchandise that is old to him, but still new to the public.

*Mini-Listings:* Throughout the Bay Area there are little shops tucked away on side streets or located in small shopping centers that offer good savings on their merchandise. However, their selection may be so small compared to the other stores listed in the previous category that though people in their area should be made aware of them, it would be unrealistic to drive 30-50 miles to pay them a visit. Circle those in your area. If you're 10-15 minutes away you should not overlook these nearby resources.

## Factory Outlets

### THE APPAREL FACTORY
1272 El Camino, San Carlos 94070. Phone: 592-1515. Hours: M-F 10am-8pm, Sat 10am-5pm, Sun 12pm-5pm. Purchases: BA, MC, Parking: Lot.

Other Store: 2150 Shattuck Ave., Berkeley.

Where is one most likely to find an unlimited selection of Ditto pants? Why at the factory outlet stores, of course. An outlet in a grand way, the store is pleasantly decorated in a country-casual way. There is an overwhelming selection of those "famous for the fit" pants in girls sizes, 7-pre-teen, Junior girls, 3-13, and Misses, 8-16.

While I have found pants priced lower at a few other stores, the attraction here is the unlimited selection in every style and color. A typical tag reads, "Selected imperfects with suggested retail price $16.00, our price $11.20." All seem first quality to me with few noticeable flaws. Self-service prevails but there are plenty of salesgirls to keep the stock in order.

Along with Dittos they are starting to carry fashions from other top California manufacturers like Wayne Rodgers, Genesis and Tom Boy, passing on saving of 30-60%. The men's selection is small and limited to shirts at this time; but they're planning to add more lines as they become available.

## APRON & LINEN FACTORY OUTLET

2200 Zanker Road, San Jose. Phone: (408) 263-8300. Purchases: MC, BA. Hours: M-F 8am-4pm, Sat 10am-4pm. Parking: Lot.

No, you're not in the wrong neighborhood—not if you're looking for bargains. True, this industrial park is an unlikely area for a factory outlet but this apron and linen outlet is a surprise in many ways. The merchandise is beautifully displayed and neatly organized. All the delightful kitchen and gourmet aprons are displayed on racks. The oven mitts, pot holders, kitchen towels, tablecloths, placemats and napkins are arranged neatly on shelves and tables. Everything made by this manufacturer is from good quality cotton and polyester blends that wash beautifully and are permanent press.

I did all my Xmas shopping for the women in my family here last year. I took real pleasure in buying the "little luxuries" they're too practical to buy for themselves. Samples, imperfects and discontinued lines are sent to the outlet from the factory next door. Savings range from 40-70% off. They are expanding their line to include hostess and leisure apparel. I spotted some lovely skirts and tops which would give any woman confidence as she prepares to entertain.

## DISCOUNT FACTORY OUTLET

201 Bayshore Blvd., San Francisco. Phone: 982-4677. Hours: M-F 9:30am-4pm, Sat 9am-2pm. Purchases: Cash only. Parking: Street.

You'll hasten up the stairs to their second-floor outlet when you see the manufacturer's name (Tami Sportswear) on the outside of the building. This line of sportswear is very well known and appeals to the ladies who like basic good fashion (nothing too faddish or fancy, just good wardrobe basics). There is a nice selection of skirts, sweaters, pants and blouses. Prices are 40-50% off retail even though most of the garments are current in-season fashions.

Bring plenty of cash or you'll be out of luck when you get to the cash register. Sizes range from 6-16. There were many sweaters in large sizes (something usually hard to find).

## CREAM JEANS OUTLET
(See **Men's Clothing**)

## THE ELEGANT COAT & DRESS OUTLET

2701 16th St., San Francisco 94103. Phone: 863-2720. Hours: Sat 8am-noon. Purchases: BA, MC. Parking: Street.

This factory store for a leading name-brand ladies' coat and dress manufacturer offers first-quality and irregular garments at wholesale prices. The styles are truly elegant, more suited to the mature woman who desires that expensive look. The coats, with their fur trims, capes, and fancy fabrics, are a little much for the casual, suburban way of life, but fine for more formal lifestyles. There are many lovely coat and dress ensembles with exquisite design and tailoring, as well as many bright-colored all-weather coats in vinyls and suedes.

This manufacturer sells his line in only the most exclusive stores and shops. You probably won't find anything here in their first-quality in-season garments for under $75, and that's their wholesale price!

In a separate room you'll find damaged clothing for up to 75% off. "Damaged" means that some clothing may be soiled, flawed, or sized improperly. There were many beautiful coats that were super bargains if a talented seamstress could finish the collars, which were only partially sewn together. Of course, selection and size are limited in this room, and no exchanges or returns are accepted. The fabric room offers elegant pre-cut fabrics, clearly labeled as to fiber content and length, at wholesale prices.

Twice I found the door to the factory store locked; when this happens, the only entry is through the employees' entrance (security guards cheerfully direct one to the outlet rooms). It's a good idea to call during the week to make sure the factory store is open.

## EMERYVILLE CLOTHING & FABRIC OUTLET
1711 64th St., (Next to Fwy 80), Emeryville 94608. Phone: 547-3555. Hours: M-F 10am-4pm. Parking: Street.

Soft, feminine fashions in dresses, blouses and skirts are proving very popular for all those trekking here, to one of the newest factory outlets in the Bay Area. For Juniors, the sun dresses, blouse and skirt combinations are delightful and easy on the budget. For the Misses sizes, caftans, hostess skirts and dresses, street dresses and blouses give the mature woman the feeling she's catered to by a manufacturer who realizes there are a lot of ladies in the 12-18 size range who appreciate a good bargain. These garments are samples, overruns, irregulars with the biggest selection in sample size 10. Savings are 40-60% off retail.

Fabrics from their sewing rooms, as well as notions (zippers, buttons, cording and trims) are available in a good selection at give-away prices. A poly-wool challis print, 60″ wide was a steal for $3.00 a yard when compared to the $6.00 a yard price for 45″ width at a local fabric store. Bags of quilting scraps are super buys. Before leaving, have your name put on their mailing list so you can catch their last-chance sales.

## FACTORY OUTLET STORE
101 15th Street, San Francisco 94103. Phone: 864-8700 ext. 18. Hours: M-F 9am-4pm, Sat 9am-2pm. Purchases: BA, MC.

Other Stores: 654 Sacramento St. 2nd fl. San Francisco.

Lucky for all of us, woe to the manufacturer, there is always a certain amount of clothing that has to be marked irregular or seconds, styles are discontinued, or estimates on production are not exact and there is an excess of clothing. So, this manufacturer has joined other Bay Area manufacturers in opening an outlet store to minimize losses.

There are several popular labels (Terri Petite, Terri Juniors, Arnel of California and 16th Street), represented in the Junior and Petite sizes ranging from 5-13. Both mom and daughters can shop here and both will be pleased with the prices (approx. 40-60% below retail). There are blouses, jeans, gowns, dresses, and jumpers in cottons, jerseys, and polyesters, as well as left over fabrics from their sewing rooms. Dressing rooms are available.

## FACTORY SAMPLE OUTLET
165 8th St. (1st floor) between Mission and Howard, San Francisco. Hours: Fri only 11am-2:30pm. Purchases: Cash. Parking: Street.

This is a very small factory store. I wouldn't drive 25 miles just to shop here unless you have other outlets to visit in the area. Also, take note that they're only open on Fridays. This manufacturer makes sweaters in many styles and under different labels; Zado is most familiar to Bay Area buyers. There are Juniors, Misses, and Large sizes. The styles vary from the grandmothers-cardigan type to pullovers and funky mod sweater sets. They had many bulky cardigans in the tweedy look popular this year. The outlet is located on the first floor just inside the main entrance. Savings average about 50% off.

## FACTORY STORE
111 Texas St., San Francisco 94107. Phone: 864-1164. Hours: M-F 9am-5pm, Sat 9am-3pm. Parking: Street. Purchases: Cash only.

This has to be one of my favorite factory outlets. It's the primary outlet for a well-known San Francisco manufacturer, Shirtworks and Tea Party. You'll never buy another blouse or sweater at a retail store after shopping here. All garments are marked second or irregular. The irregulars are the best buy because their flaws are practically indiscernable. The seconds are lower priced; you should give them the onceover because there are no returns or exchanges. They have dressier blouses in beautiful polyester silk-like prints and solids as well as T-shirts, and soft cotton blouses in many styles.

Several times a year they post a sale sign on their window and everything is marked down an additional $1.00-$5.00. Prices range from $3.00-$20.00 on most of their clothing. Sizes range from 5-13.

Both mothers and teenage daughters will like these styles, but if you shop on Saturday be prepared for the crush of bodies struggling in and out of clothes in the dressing rooms.

## G.S. FACTORY OUTLET

524 2nd Street (2nd floor) San Francisco 94107. Phone: 495-3326. Hours: M-Sat 9am-4:30pm. Purchases: Cash, Check. Parking: Street (limited).

This is where all my younger friends go to buy long party dresses, prom dresses, etc. This is a Junior line in sizes 5-13. Fathers are delighted at the savings. Irregulars, samples, overruns are approximately 50% off, sometimes 75% or more on very irregular garments. Often a handy seamstress can repair those irregularities, then glow over her super bargain. There are blouses and short dresses in the same general styles and fabulous buys on fabrics (laces, cottons, and voiles in lovely colors). You can't return these dresses, so be sure you can fix (or live with) the flaws before taking your purchases home.

## THE GREAT BLOUSE & SEPARATES OUTLET

208, 218 and 244 Fremont St., San Francisco 94105. Phone: 986-4133. Hours: M-F 10am-4:30pm, Sat 9am-4pm. Purchases: Cash, Local Checks. Parking: Street (limited).

I cut my teeth on bargain hunting at this outlet store. The labels, Fritzi (Misses sizes) and You Babes (Junior sizes) are very popular with Bay Area bargain sleuths. Recently they've added dressing rooms which takes the guesswork out of buying their dresses, tops, pants, skirts and jumpsuits.

The long popularity of this outlet can only be attributed to the low prices, 40-70% off on their 2nds, irregulars, and overruns. Flaws are usually marked with masking tape and sometimes I've had the price knocked down further when

I've found a flaw they've missed. They have frequent end-of-season and overstock sales. All sales are final so check garments carefully before buying.

## KORET CLOTHES OUTLET

360 Florida St., San Francisco 94110. Phone: 957-2289. Hours: M-F 9am-4pm; Sat 9am-1pm. Purchases: Cash, check. Parking: Lot.

Look for the bright yellow sign over the door and you've arrived at one of my favorite places. There is a vast selection of all Koret garments as well as samples and over-runs from other manufacturers like White Stag, Alex Coleman, Stage VII, Solo, Bleeker Street and Givenchy. Most of the clothing is appealing to the mature woman (over 30) who finds Koret fashions more durable and lasting in her wardrobe than some of the more trendy manufacturers. There are dressing rooms and the prices are marked on the underside of the label. Sizes range from 8-20 on these 2nds, samples and overruns. Savings are 30-70% off retail prices.

The men are not overlooked here. After you put your new wardrobe together you'll want to look over the men's racks that feature good buys on sport shorts, sweaters, raincoats, slacks and other items. Ski wear has been available from top European manufacturers this last year at very good prices. Before leaving give the fabric selection the once over just to make sure you've scouted all the bargain potentials. Fabrics are sold at 50% savings, with buttons and remnants at a discount too. Polyesters, wools, cottons, and jerseys (prints and plains) are available in generous widths.

## M.C.O.

675 East Brokaw Road (Freeway 17 & Brokaw) San Jose (Brokaw Business Park). Phone: 279-3855. Hours: M-F 10am-6pm, Sat 10am-4pm. Purchases: Cash, check. Parking: Lot.

New Store: 5759 Pacheco Blvd. (1 mile north of Sun Valley Shopping Center), Pacheco 94553. Hours: M-Sat 10am-6pm, Th & F evenings till 9pm.

Finally! One of the major San Francisco manufacturers has realized that San Jose and South Bay shoppers love bargains as much as anyone else, but that they may not have the time or inclination to drive 40+ miles into the City, so they've opened an outlet right in their backyard.

You'll recognize the labels immediately in all their ladies fashions, their own fine label (Koret of Calif.) as well as famous maker closeouts they buy up as they become available. Size ranges are from 6-46 (of course the selection in larger sizes is much smaller). You'll often find ski-wear, pro shop lines of tennis togs, costume jewelry, designer scarves along with the dresses, separates, sweaters, and coordinated lines of sportswear. Men's clothes are stocked occasionally when the buyer can pull a coup and snap up some great lines and labels in shirts, sweaters, jackets, and pants. There is a communal dressing room and a separate dressing room for men. Savings are a sublime 30-70% off on these irregulars, samples and overruns. All sales are final.

## THE OUTLET STORE

221 So. Maple, South San Francisco. Phone: 761-1467. Hours: T-Fri 10am-4pm, Sat 9am-40m. Purchases: Cash, check. Parking: Lot.

You really have to go out of your way to find this factory outlet so I'm including directions on how to get there. Take Bayshore Fwy. South to Grand Ave., turn west, turn left on Linden, right on Victory and left on South Maple. The outlet is adjacent to the factory.

Moms and teens can shop here together if they're between sizes 6-16. Pants, skirts, sweaters and blouses predominate in the selection of samples and overruns from the factory warehouse. There is a rack at the back with irregulars at super low prices. Occasionally, when I've wanted something in a different color the salespeople have been able to round it up from their stockroom. Most of their fashions, made in synthetics and cottons, are seen prominently displayed in retail stores.

## RAINCOAT OUTLET

543 Howard St., San Francisco 94105. Phone: 362-2626. Hours: M-F 8am-4pm, Sat 8am-2pm. Purchases: BA, MC. Parking: Street.

A rarity, an elegant outlet, complete with beautiful and stylish all-weather coats, suit jackets, pants, matching hats and velveteen coats. This prestige line is sold in the "best" stores at those "best store" prices. Wholesale prices at the outlet usually start around $40.00 on the samples, discontinued, and factory overruns. If you're lucky you may find a super buy on their $10 rack which features "tired" coats. The size range is particularly accommodating, 4-24. Occasionally I have found that the doors to the outlet are closed; however, if you want to shop you can go up the stairs to the office and someone will probably open the doors and give you a chance to browse around.

## REDWOOD CITY KNITTING MILLS AND FABRIC OUTLET

150 Charter Street, (near Gemco) Redwood City. Phone: 364-9890. Purchases: Cash, check. Hours: M-F 10am-4pm, Sat 9:30am-12:30pm. Parking: Street.

Not everyone knows what to do with a sweater body, but for those women who have been involved with "stretch and sew" techniques this is an opportunity to buy sweater fabric that can be made into a sweater that truly looks "store bought".

This sweater manufacturer puts left-over knit pieces in his factory store that have a 1″ rib edge on the bottom (perfect for sleeve and body edges) and saves you the task of trying to hem the sweater with that perfect finished look. Fabrics sell for $3.00/#. You can also rummage through his scrap boxes to find matching trims. For the larger woman who despairs at finding a decent sweater in sizes 36-52 at a reasonable price, there is a nice selection of discontinued, sample and irregular sweaters. Best of all, they're sold at wholesale prices!

## Retail Stores

Bargains in Samples, Overruns, Closeouts, and Irregulars.

### AARON'S
(See **Men's Clothing**)

### CAPWELL'S BUDGET STORE
(See **Family Clothing**)

### CASA SPINALI
(See **Men's Clothing**)

### THE CLOTHES BIN
20650 Stevens Creek Blvd., (Cupertino Crossroads Center), Cupertino. Phone: 252-9751. Hours: M-F 10am-9pm, Sat 10am-6pm, Sun 12pm-5pm. Purchases: BA, MC, FN.

Other Stores: San Francisco, Eastmont Mall, Oakland, Redwood City; in San Jose: Plaza Shopping Center, Cambrian Plaza, Almaden Fashion Plaza.

This is one of seven stores located in the Bay Area selling nationally advertised brands of sportswear and dresses at 20-60% discounts. These bargains are made possible by several methods: Some of the clothes are closeouts or overruns which are purchased way below wholesale; another method is in-season volume buying, (most retailers buy way in advance of the season). There are more dresses and coats in the Oakland and San Francisco stores. Although their size range is 5/6 to 15/16, at this time they seem to have more in the 12-16 size range. They do have a liberal lay-a-way and return policy with a no-hassle attitude almost anyone would appreciate.

## THE CLOTHES CIRCUIT

120 Petticoat Lane, Walnut Creek 94596. Phone: 933-0300. Hours: M-F 10am-9pm, Sat 10am-6pm, Sun 12am-5pm. Purchases: BA, MC, VISA. Parking: Private Lot.

Other Store: Pleasant Hill (K-Mart Shopping Center).

If you need a dress for church or an important daytime occasion and you're lucky enough to wear sample sizes 8-12, go no further, this is the place! *Clothes Circuit* obtains the salesman's samples from the "Who's Who" of apparel makers. Prices are reduced about 30% from the retail price on these garments. For the girls and ladies in sizes 6-16 in Juniors and Misses there is quite a selection of coordinated sportswear. The men's section is well stocked with casual pants, shirts, sweaters, and jackets. *Clothes Circuit* also has a few racks of merchandise that other stores don't seem to bother with; namely, ski pants, powder pants, ski jackets for the whole family, swimwear, tennis togs and golf clothes. I've had good luck finding children's parkas and jackets from the best manufacturers and have really appreciated the 30% discount. They have very good sales during January and July and will mail advance notices to customers who request this info. You won't miss this store if you look for *Lipperts Ice Cream Parlor* first and then look further back to the parking lot area.

## THE CLOTHES RACK

1043 4th St., San Rafael 94901. Phone: 456-2646. Hours: M-Sat 11am-6pm, Sun noon-5pm. Parking: Lot. Purchases: Cash, check.

Other Stores: Berkeley, Campbell, Citrus Heights, Concord, Davis, Oakland, Sacramento, San Francisco, San Jose, San Leandro, Walnut Creek.

*The Clothes Rack* is really plain, decor-wise, that is. They prefer to save expenses by cutting down on the frills and letting their fashion selection do all the dazzling. They buy all the right looks from those big names who often make too much of a good thing. These overruns are bought by the rack-full at substantial savings that they pass on—so that you can buy by the rack-full too. Racks of new pants, skirts, tops, dresses, sweaters, coats and accessories arrive continuously to keep the young contemporary fashion-conscious woman in style with prices that range from $2.00-$60.00. Their size range accommodates Jrs., Misses, and Woman's sizes. To be sure, this is not the place to bring your boyfriend or husband. There's no place for them to wait while you mosey through the racks. They also have a 30-day lay-a-way policy.

## DANBURY LTD.

120 East Prospect Ave., Danville 94526. Phone: 837-3777. Hours: M-Sat 10am-5:30pm. Purchases: BA, MC. Parking: Street.

This obscure little boutique offers women's and career girl fashions. It's patronized particularly by women in their 30's who like the look of class and sophistication. *Danbury* is a sample shop with the biggest selection in sizes 8-10. Some 10's in their better lines fit 12's beautifully.

Their selection changes frequently, often they get sample merchandise before it's shown in local prestige and hi-fashion stores. I've seen fine designer lines on their racks like John Meyer, Austin Hill and Patty Woodard, great for career-conscious girls. They also have samples in lingerie and bathing suits.

They keep a mailing list for active customers who want to be the first to know when new designer merchandise has arrived. Savings on samples are approximately a third.

## EHRENBERG BROS.

140 Geary St., (6th floor), San Francisco 94108. Phone: 362-6636. Hours: M-F 9:30am-5:30pm, Sat 9:30am-4:30pm. Purchases: BA, MC. Parking: Pay lot.

If you love to shop in the truly elegant stores but the prices don't fit in your budget, take heart. *Ehrenberg Bros.* offers the very same clothes at a 20-40% savings off current retail prices. *Ehrenberg Bros.* carry only first quality garments, all are either labeled or have the manufacturers hang tag. Their sixth floor showrooms boast racks and racks of current in-season, highly fashionable coats, dresses, furs, pantsuits, raincoats, sportswear and accessories. In their fur department you will be able to see one of the largest fur selections in San Francisco. It is truly a pleasure to shop in these well organized showrooms with its air of refinement. They will ship your purchases anywhere. Visitors are always welcome, shop leisurely.

## EMPORIUM BARGAIN BASEMENT
(See **Linens**)

## THE FACTORY STORE

20 2nd St., San Francisco 94105. Phone: 495-4783. Hours: M-Sat 10:30am-5:30pm. Purchases: BA, MC. Parking: Street, pay lots.

You'll fine things here from well-known San Francisco manufacturers of boutique clothing. Blouses and sweaters, pants, dresses, and pantsuits range in price from $5 to $30, which represents savings of as much as 50% on some merchandise. All the proceeds from this store support a local charity. There's a communal dressing room, in keeping with the bare-bones atmosphere. Some of the clothing is irregular or seconds, and the merchandise is strictly "as is." Sorry, no returns or exchanges.

## THE FACTORY STORE

722 San Anselmo Ave., San Anselmo 94960. Phone: 453-5624. Hours: M-Sat 10am-5:15pm. Purchases: BA, MC. Parking: Street.

Other Store: 971 Grand Ave., San Rafael.

Many people would love to have this store owner's connections. Levi's ladies pants, skirts, jumpers and tops are brought in from the factory and sold at 40-50% savings. The size range is 3-18. Irregular is stamped on a large portion of the merchandise, but the flaws are minor. Other garments, that are first quality, are overruns. All the clothes are nicely displayed.

## FASHION FACTORY

10730 San Pablo Ave., El Cerrito 94530. Phone: 525-3733. Hours: M-S 9:30am-5:30pm. Purchases: BA, MC. Parking: Lot.

*Fashion Factory* features hundreds of women's garments in sizes 8-20. The styles are up-to-date but with appeal primarily to mature women...not much for Junior-sized "mod" ladies. The brand names are well known (Koret, Murr, Catalina and Graff etc.) and the garments are in excellent condition (no seconds or irregulars). The store is clean and well organized with dressing rooms and exchange privileges. Savings average around 30%.

## THE GOLD HANGER

1711 Santa Rita Rd. (Amador Center), Pleasanton 94550. Phone: 846-4653. Hours: M-F 9:30am-9pm, Sat 9:30am-5:30pm. Sun 11am-5pm. Purchases:BA, MC. Parking: Lot.

Other Stores: Campbell, San Jose, San Leandro, Santa Clara.

If you're a petite 4'11" and your best friend is a robust 5'10" you probably have trouble shopping in the same stores. At Gold Hanger you can both shop successfully. The emphasis here is depth. Sizes range from 3 petite to 18 tall, and regardless of your height or girth you're bound to find something in their proportioned sizes.

There is a large selection of casual clothing (tops and bottoms) in current, popular fashions in all the "in" colors. The merchandise is unbranded (which means this is budget merchandise for budget clothing stores) but they take a lower mark-up and their prices are 15-25% less than other budget stores. Even though these are budget brands I found the selection very pleasing and regardless of the price the clothes look like they cost more. They had some great prices on accessories, jewelry, scarves, and belts. I often find that these little items put the biggest dent in my clothing budget. Unlike so many bargain stores they will provide a box and bow—nice for gift giving—and also make exchanges.

## J.P.J. CALIFORNIA FASHION FACTORY OUTLETS

825 W. Hamilton, Campbell 95008. Phone: 374-1790. Hours: M-F 10am-9pm, Sat 10am-6pm, Sun 11am-5pm. Purchases: BA, MC.

Other Stores: San Bruno, San Jose, Sunnyvale, Hayward, Redwood City.

*J.P.J.* has 24 stores in California with 7 here in the Bay Area. All the merchandise is manufacturer's overruns. The labels are cut, but at 30-60% savings this little omission won't bother you. Sizes range from 5/6 to 15/16. This is one of those stores you'll want to check out regularly so you'll be able to snatch up the choicest merchandise as it arrives. Separates, skirts, pants, blouses, etc. are featured in their selection.

## JUDY'S FASHIONS

124 Front St., San Francisco 94111. Phone: 731-3221. Hours: M-F 10am-5:30pm. Purchases: BA, MC. Parking: Pay lot.

This is a shopping mecca for the working girl in the financial district. While luxury-store services like gift wrapping and attentive clerks are missing here, the self-service approach enables *Judy's* to offer great savings on a large selection of sample merchandise, irregulars, closeouts, and discontinued styles. Dressing rooms are plentiful—a welcome change from most bargain clothes outlets!

Whatever your style, you're likely to find something here. Bathing suits, pants, tops, dresses, accessories, and a similar selection of men's clothing are all on hand for browsing. Savings on special merchandise will range from 20-50%. They also carry merchandise at regular prices to insure an adequate shopping selection at all times. New merchandise is always arriving, which must account for the crowd of eager buyers at lunchtime. Be sure to leave the price tag intact if you are likely to return the garment; no refunds or exchanges will be made otherwise.

## K & E DEPARTMENT STORE

2226 Taraval Street, San Francisco (Betw. 32nd & 33rd Ave.). Phone: 731-3321. Hours: M-Sat 9am-6pm. Purchases: BA, MC. Parking: Street.

Plan to spend some time at *K & E* or forget it! It's a real hodge podge of ladies' and younger women's clothing. The racks are simply jammed with merchandise and the chaos can be unnerving. You'll find bathing suits, lingerie, aprons, leisurewear, bathrobes, jogging suits, skirts, dresses, pants, blouses and accessories. Sizes range from 6-18 and 5-15. Some of the merchandise is irregular and priced accordingly. For all the chaos there seems to be many faithful shoppers who don't mind weeding through the racks to dig out those super buys that reflect savings of 40-70% off. This is one store that has a fairly good selection for larger women.

## KAYE FASHIONS

873 North San Matio Drive, San Mateo 94401. Phone: 347-2533. Purchases: MC, BA, VISA. Hours: T-F 10am-6pm, Sat 10am-5pm.

*Kaye Fashions* has a low-key existence off the beaten path. Most of the garments appear to be overruns, closeouts and samples. Most intriguing were the labels, usually found in exclusive shops and better stores. I saw many Paganne, Diane von Furstenburg, Geoffrey Beene, Nik-Nik, Shayne Leathers etc. The only touch of class here is the clothing because the store is simply unadorned, lacking the fancy atmosphere usually surrounding clothes of this quality.

Most of the fashions will be perfect for the mature ladies who find themselves overlooked by so many Junior conscious boutiques and their far out fashions. On my last visit there were several racks of men's sport shirts at almost wholesale prices. Dressing rooms are available.

**LINGERIE FABRIC OUTLET**
(See **Fabrics**)

**LOEHMANN'S**
75 Westlake Mall, Daly City 94015. Phone: 755-2424. Hours: M-Sat 10am-5:30pm, Wed 10am-9:30pm. Purchases: Cash, check. Parking: Lot.

Other Store: 1651 Hollenbeck Ave., Sunnyvale 94087.

*Loehmann's* has been famous for over 55 years on the East Coast for quality fashions at great savings. Yes, they are a branch of the Loehmann's in New York City and Boston. They've been so successful that they now have 34 stores across the United States. Their clothing is the better designer-type; many are samples and overruns.

Their Daly City store has a no frills appearance that is in direct contrast to the exciting selection of clothing sold here. There are all types of "mood" clothes—cocktail, dressy, furs, in-between, sportswear; and those of you clever enough to recognize designer clothes without a label will find fashions from Geoffrey Beene, Adele Simpson, Bill Blass, Ann Klein and others of equal renown.

Inflation fighters will want to sharpen their nails and develop their aggressiveness to hang on to their "finds". Their communal dressing rooms always seem a bit hectic (like a dressing room for a dance company with two minutes to change for their next number). You can be sure that you'll save at least ⅓ off the retail price, and often 50% or more.

**MAGNARAMA (JOSEPH MAGNIN)**
Westlake Shopping Center, Daly City 94105. Phone 772-2705. Hours: MTThSat 10am-5:30pm, W&F 10am-9pm. Purchases: BA, MC, Store charge. Parking: Lot.

A collection of "leftovers" from all the Joseph Magnin stores in the Bay Area is here at *Magnarama.* Feel sorry for the clothes—they were rejected by buyers at their original retail prices—but feel happy for yourself: you reap the savings! These ultra-fashionable clothes have already been on sale once in the regular JM departments, but were relegated to the *Magnarama* racks when they didn't sell. So prices have been slashed once, twice, thrice, as the price tag shows. Each time the price is reduced they cross out the former one, which delights me—I'm always much more pleased with a bargain buy when I can compare the sale price with the original. There's a certain amount of ego satisfaction at having beat the system.

You'll find the savings can amount to a whopping 50%. Examine the goods before purchase; there may be a missing button, belt, snap, pulled or ripped seam, or some other flaw (then again, lots of the clothes are in perfect condition). All sales are final; there are no exchanges or refunds.

## MANUFACTURER'S OUTLET STORE

344 California Ave., Palo Alto 94306. Phone: 321-4385. Hours: M-Sat 10am-5:30pm, 10am-6:30pm. Purchases: BA, MC. Parking: Street.

For ladies with conventional good taste here is a little shop just for you. Coordinated sportswear is the specialty with several popular well-known brands represented. Sizes range from 8-20 in Misses and 3-15 in Junior selections. Regular merchandise is reduced 25%, irregulars (a small proportion of the total selection) are 40% off, and manufacturer's overruns are usually 30% off. They have sales in January and August—don't miss them!

## MARSHALL'S
(See **Family Clothing**)

## MATERNITY FACTORY OUTLET

2304 S. El Camino Real (½ mile north of Hillsdale Shopping Center), San Mateo 94403. Phone: 341-3747. Hours: MTh 10am-9pm, TWFSat 10am-6pm, Sun 12am-5pm. Purchases: BA, MC.

Other Store: 106 Petticoat Lane, Walnut Creek.

For the lady-in-waiting who would like to be fashionable at budget prices, this outlet (the only maternity outlet in the Bay Area) offers many opportunities to save money. I just loved the younger fashion look of the clothes, and the selection in pants, dresses, tops, coordinated separates, evening wear and lingerie. This Chicago manufacturer distributes to his own outlets, eliminating the middle man and some retail frills. Savings range from 25-50%. Sales occur regularly and provide even greater savings for the "expectant mother".

## MERCHANDISERS INC.
(See **Men's Clothing**)

## N.A.N.C.Y.'S FASHION CLEARANCE

4220 Broadway, Oakland 94611. Hours: M-Fri 10am-6:00 pm; Sat 9-5:30pm. Purchases: BA, MC, VISA. Parking: Street.

East Bay ladies will be delighted with the selection of clothing displayed at this store. Merchandise is made available through special purchase from many manufacturers; most are overruns. They also carry close-outs from local department stores and there is a wide range of styles and qualities represented. I saw many prestigious labels among the clothes. The biggest selection can be found in their separates; however, they do have some dresses and suits. There is a limited selection of children's clothing. The savings range from 40-75% off retail prices. There are dressing rooms available and the atmosphere and decor is certainly posh compared to most outlet stores. Size range in ladies clothing is 6-16.

## PANTS O/OFF
(See **Men's Clothing**)

## PAUL'S DEPARTMENT STORE
(See **Part II: Damaged Freight Outlets**)

## PIC-A-DILLY
1847 El Camino Real, Burlingame Plaza, Burlingame. Phone: 697-9846. Purchases: Cash, check.

Other Stores: Belmont, Campbell, Capitola, Concord, Fremont, Los Gatos, Menlo Park, Mountain View, Salinas, San Anselmo, and San Jose.

*Pic-a-dilly* buys overruns of current fashion apparel, the same fashions you buy in the big stores. Their New York buyers are "in the market" every day. Fashions are shipped direct to the Bay Area for distribution in their 13 stores. Of course, they cut the labels to protect the manufacturer, but do you really care if you can save $$$? The savings are worth shouting about, 30-50% off, and they are marked down even more the longer they hang on the racks. Quick turnover is a must to maintain low prices. Stop in frequently when you're shopping for blouses, dresses, swimwear, skirts, pants, even tennis togs. Their fashion range has appeal from the most mod gal to the basically conservative matron. Among my friends who shop there is my 16-year-old babysitter and a 57-year-old neighbor! The stores are all self-service, simple and clean.

## RAGSMATAZZ
2036 Union St., San Francisco. Phone: 563-1398. Hours: M-Sat 11am-6pm, Sun 12am-5pm. Purchases: BA, MC. Parking: Street.

Other Stores: Moraga, Napa, Oakland, San Anselmo.

Don't think you have the wrong place just because this store doesn't look like the typical bargain store. It is uniquely located on a lower level next door to the Delancey Street Restaurant. I think it's worth a trip from just about any place in the Bay Area because the merchandise is so beautifully organized and displayed. Most of the clothing here is categorized as manufacturers' overruns. All are first-quality, popular brands (sorry I can't mention specific labels; you'll recognize them) and the prices are great! About 40% off. For example, $18.00 blouses for $9.95, $22.00 pants for $11.00. Also pantsuits, dresses, denims, blazers, gowns, pants, blouses, and T-shirts. Junior sizes only 3-13. At these prices all sales are final. Parking along Union Street is always a problem. Good luck!

## S & R FASHION CENTER
2058 Mission Street, San Francisco 94110. Phone: 626-0856. Hours: M-Sat 11am-6pm, Sun 12am-5pm. Parking: Street. Purchases: Cash, check.

Only the most dedicated bargain hunters will enjoy shopping at *S & R*. This is a last post outlet for many Bay Area manufacturers. You'll find out of season, overruns, irregulars all jammed onto racks in such a manner that few have the patience to look for that super buy amidst the clutter.

The prices are an inducement to persevere: up to 70% off on their range of fashions that will suit juniors through matrons. Parking can be a problem at this Mission Street location. I've picked up a few parking tickets when my five minute excursion lasted an hour or longer.

## THE SAMPLE CELL
1896 Second Street, Concord 94520. Phone: 689-1558. Hours: M-Sat 10am-5:30pm. Purchases: BA, MC. Parking: Lot.

Other Stores: Moraga, Livermore, Danville.

For lovely ladies dresses and sportswear, *The Sample Cell* is a must on your shopping list. "A sample" is usually one garment made (not manufactured) in the designing room with fabric, trim, and workmanship much, much superior to any stock garment. An "original sample" is a priceless, "one-of-a-kind" work of art worth many times the price for it. A "sample discard" is a garment never duplicated because it was not selected for manufacture. A "duplicate sample" is one of two to eight garments (one for each salesman) made to show to buyers.

At *The Sample Cell* the original wholesale tag is left on, you add $2.00 to arrive at your purchase price. Most garments are size 10. This should not discourage 8-12's or junior sizes 9-11 from giving them a try. Tens can run large or small depending upon the manufacturer.

## SOFT TOUCH FACTORY STORE
501 Bryant, San Francisco 94107. Phone: 495-5940. Hours: M-Sat 10am-5pm. Purchases: BA, MC. Parking: Street.

I was pleasantly surprised at the selection of clothing on the racks in this freshly painted and re-organized outlet. Along with the usual San Francisco manufacturers there are many lines brought in from Los Angeles like Jag, CoCo, and Malibu Media. This store will appeal to career oriented young woman who want more than just casual sportswear. There are even some bargain priced accessories. Dressing rooms and lay-a-way privileges make selection and buying very easy. Sizes range from 3-16 in their dresses, separates and coordinated fashions. They had a fine selection of wools, khaki's and velvets that are not as available in other outlets.

## SOMETHING SPECIAL
31 Bovet Road, San Mateo. Phone: 574-7771. Hours: M-F 9:30am-7pm, Sat 9:30am-6pm, Sun 12pm-5pm. Purchases: BA, MC.

Other Stores: Burlingame and San Rafael.

This store is popular with Peninsula working girls for its first quality separates and coordinated sportswear at factory store prices. Sizes range from 3-13. I particularly like their selection of accessories, something most outlet stores don't bother with. All the merchandise is nicely displayed and the sales staff couldn't be more accommodating.

## SPORTIQUE FASHIONS

2310 Homestead Rd., Foothill Plaza, Los Altos. Phone: 735-8660. Hours: M-F 9:30am-9pm, Sat 9:30am-6pm, Sun 12am-5pm. Purchases: BA, MC.

Other Stores: Princeton Plaza, San Jose; Alpha Beta Center, Sunnyvale/Saratoga Roads, San Jose.

The very first thing you want to do at *Sportique* is get on their mailing list! They have super sales 6-8 times a year—the biggest on New Year's Day.

*Sportique* has a very versatile selection of clothing for teens and women. Sizes range in Junior and Misses from 3-20. All the popular brands, local and nationally known favorites, are represented in current styles at savings of 30-60% below prevailing retail. Best of all, they don't cut their labels. Their prices almost compare to the factory outlets in the City. There are no returns on sale items but you have 4 days for cash refunds on regular merchandise. These are all first-quality garments . . . and I have no doubt that I'd be a regular if this store were closer to me!

## THE UPPER HALF

351 Main Street, Los Altos 94022. Phone: 948-8890. Hours: M-Sat 10am-6pm, T 10am-7pm. Purchases: BA, MC. Parking: Street.

If you like elegantly tailored sportswears—the kind you find at Saks or I. Magnin, in gorgeous cottons, polyesters, silks and woolens, you'll love *The Upper Half,* a discount store for the "upper class". The designer labels are cut off but if you're label conscious you'll be able to recognize the merchandise. The sizes cater to the smaller ladies (3-16) though there are a few nods to the larger gals.

There are few irregulars in the selection, most are first quality overruns or samples. This is a fine resource for the more mature lady. Catch their sales by getting on their mailing list because your average 30% savings can be up to 60% at these times. There is ample parking behind the store. Dressing rooms and exchange privileges.

# Mini-Listings

## BARBARA'S CLOTHES BOUTIQUE

4554 Glenmoor Mall (Eggers & Logan Dr.), Fremont. Phone: 792-5222. Hours: M-F 11am-6pm, Sat 11am-5pm, Thurs eve till 8pm. Purchases: MC, BA. Parking: Lot.

First quality overruns and samples in Misses and Junior sizes 5-18. Sportswear, long and short dresses, pants, and sweaters at 30-40% off.

## CASTRO PUT-ONS

89 Estates Drive, Danville 94526. Phone: 837-8537. Hours: T-F 10am-5pm, Sat 12pm-5pm. Purchases: BA, MC. Parking: Street.

Located in a small cottage behind Danville Auto Parts, this store sells Jr. & Misses, sizes 5-18 in sportswear, and long and short dresses at savings of 35-60% off.

## CLOTHES CITY

4856 El Camino Real, Los Altos 94022. Phone: 964-2200. Hours: M-S 9:30am-6pm, Sun 12pm-5pm. Purchases: BA, MC. Parking: Lot.

Other Store: San Rafael.

A small discount store with fashions like Faded Glory, Cecily Sweaters, S.F. Shirtworks, that are very popular with the younger crowd. Guys and gals can pick up some super 30-40% savings on these samples, overruns and irregulars.

## CLOTHES STATION

244 Church Street (Bet. Market & 15th St.), San Francisco. Phone: 621-1626. Hours: M-S 11am-6pm. Purchases: BA, MC, VISA. Parking: Street.

A small store with Misses & Junior sizes. Clothing is geared for the younger fashion image. Dressing rooms. All sales final. Savings 30-50% off retail prices.

## FASHION JOINT

4170 Piedmont Avenue, Oakland. Phone: 655-3323. Hours: M-Sat 10am-5pm. Purchases: BA, MC, VISA. Parking: Street.

This is an unobtrusive little store in the midst of the Piedmont Avenue business district. There is a good selection of Junior sizes (5-13). Most are samples, irregulars, or freight damaged goods with savings ranging from 40-50% off retail prices.

## FACTORY SECOND STORES  (CLOTHES TO YOU)

1448 Van Ness Ave., San Francisco 94109. Phone: 474-1448. Hours: M&F 11am-5pm, TWTh 11am-6pm, Sat 12am-5pm. Purchases: BA, MC. Parking: Street.

A small outlet with manufacturers closeouts and overruns in sizes 5-13. Up to 50% discounts on pants, skirts, and blouses. Occasionally there are seconds, but they are priced accordingly.

## HOUSE OF SAMPLES

2041 El Camino Real, Santa Clara 95051. Phone: 247-4004. Hours: M-Sat 10am-5:30pm. Purchases: BA, MC, VISA. Parking: Street.

25% savings on sample fashions from many better manufacturers of Juniors and Women's sportswear.

## SAMPLE VILLAGE

2226 So. Bascom Ave., Campbell 95008. Phone: 377-6083. Hours: M-Sat 10:30am-5:30pm. Purchases: BA, MC. Parking: Lot.

Salesmen's samples of separates and dresses sell for 25-35% off. Size range 5-13.

## SECRET HANG-UPS SAMPLE BOUTIQUE

1862 Union St., San Francisco. Phone: 567-0369. Hours: M-Sat 11am-6pm, Sun 12pm-6pm, Th & F till 9pm. Purchases: BA, MC. Parking: Street, Very Difficult.

Other Stores: Mill Valley, Novato.

This is a tiny charming little shop, easily bypassed since its located upstairs at this address. The selection is small, mostly jumpers, T-shirts, pants, funky dresses and gowns. The younger girls will love these sample fashions all sold for ⅓ less than retail. Junior sizes 3-15.

## WAREHOUSE BOUTIQUE

255 4th St., Oakland 94607. Phone: 834-2075. Hours: M-Sat 10am-5:30pm. Parking: Private behind store. Purchases: BA, MC, VISA.

30-50% off Misses and Junior sizes (3-18) in dresses, pants, tops, blouses, sweaters, jackets, suits, pantsuits and cocktail dresses. Wigs sold at 25% savings and there is a nice selection of costume jewelry. Communal dressing room. All sales are final.

## THE WHITE LILY

5509 College Avenue, Oakland 94618. Phone: 547-1451. Purchases: BA, MC. Hours: M-Sat 11am-6pm. Parking: Street.

The White Lily is a small boutique-type store that sells several brands popular with the younger set: Rose Hips, Cecily Sweaters, Jasmine Tee-Shirts, Plain Jane dresses and others. Discounts range from 30-50% off. There are some irregulars. *White Lily* is just one block from the Rockridge Bart Station.

## ZOE ALLEY DISCOUNT BOUTIQUE

70 Zoe Street (off Brannan Bet. 3rd & 4th), San Francisco. Phone: 495-6975. Hours: M-F 10am-5:30pm. Purchases: BA, MC. Parking: Street.

A very small shop with some good buys on separates; blouses, pants, sweaters and skirts. Savings 25-40% off. These clothes will appeal to women with the younger fashion image.

# Cosmetics

## M. JESSUP CO.
(See **Part II: Damaged Freight Outlets**)

# Dinnerware and Accessories

(Also see **Furniture and Accessories—Catalog Discounters; General Merchandise—Catalog Discounters; Giftwares; Jewelry and Diamonds**)

## General

**AKRON**
(See **General Merchandise—Discount Stores**)

**S. CHRISTIAN OF COPENHAGEN, INC.**
225 Post Street, San Francisco 94108. Phone: 392-3394. Hours: 9:30am-6pm. Purchases: MC, BA, VISA. Parking: Pay Lots.

Other Stores: Burlingame, Palo Alto, San Jose.

Make a beeline for the best buy in the store—the crystal table with Rosenthal seconds and irregulars priced at least 50% below retail. The flaws are very slight—tiny bubbles in the glass, a size difference among pieces of a set, a few swirl marks, or the word "Rosenthal" missing from the underside of a piece. They do not, in my estimation, affect the magnificence of this marvelous hand-blown glassware in the least.

**COST PLUS IMPORTERS**
(See **General Merchandise—Discount Stores**)

**DANSK II**
Ocean Ave. & San Carlos, Carmel. Phone: 408-625-1600. Hours: Daily 9:30am-5:30pm. Purchases: Cash & Check. Parking: Street.

When manufacturers update their lines periodically it's logical that something else has to go. All discontinued merchandise from Dansk is sent to Dansk II in Carmel and is sold at a 33-66% savings. Shoppers who appreciate contemporary and functional wares will be delighted with the selection of Kobenstyle Cookware and nonconforming items: teakwood trays and salad bowls, china, stemware and bar glasses, plastics, stainless steel items, candles and candleholders. Carmel not only has charm, it has bargains!

**FARBER BROS.**
(See **Jewelry and Diamonds**)

**HEATH CERAMICS AND STONEWARE FACTORY**
400 Gate St., Sausalito 94965. Phone: 332-3732. Hours: Daily 10am-5:30pm. Purchases: Cash, Check.

Although you never need a reason to go to Sausalito, here's one that will make any visit profitable. The Heath Stoneware factory and retail store should not be overlooked by anyone who considers himself a bargain hunter. All their dishes and heat-tempered cookware that do not pass their high standards during inspection are sold for 40% below retail prices. This does not mean that they're chipped or cracked, just little flaws that the untrained eye can hardly discern. You won't find a whole set of dishes but it's likely you can fill in the missing pieces of your set at home. The selection is always changing, so more than one visit may be required to find just what you want.

## LILA'S ANTIQUES
3559 Mt. Diablo Blvd., Lafayette. Phone: 284-9017. Hours: T-Sat 10:30am-5:30pm. Purchases: BA, MC. Parking: Street.

I was referred to this small antique shop, which specializes in used sterling silver, silver hollowware, and old jewelry, by a friend who purchases several beautiful antique serving spoons for the price of only one new spoon in a modern pattern. Most of the silver patterns on display here are no longer being made, but you can probably find a pattern compatible with your own among their large selection. This is a great way to buy those soup spoons, bread and butter knives, or dessert forks you never got—at savings of about 50% off the current price of these pieces (depending a bit on the condition and weight of the sterling). Most of the silver I looked at was in beautiful condition, freshly polished and beatifully displayed in immaculate showcases. They occasionally have current patterns, too. If you are interested in a particular pattern, they will gladly take your name and notify you when and if the pieces you want come in.

There were also some very nice prices on hollowware. (Of course, very old, rare pieces are priced as collectors' items rather than as bargains.)

## M. JESSUP SALVAGE
(See **Damaged Freight Outlets**)

## SAMPLES AND SECONDS
(See **Giftwares**)

## STUDIO AND SECONDS STORE
44 Industrial Way (Behind Cost Plus), Kentfield. Phone: 924-2310. Hours: T-Sat 10am-5pm. Purchases: Cash, check. Parking: Street.

Original glassware, where each piece is handblown into contemporary designs, is perfect for people who are looking for something just a little different. You'll save 30-50% off on their pieces of stemware, candle holders, goblets, and egg-shaped paper weights that are similar to Venetian glass.

Their newest look is stemware in iridescent colors that suggests an art nouveau look. While browsing you can watch their master glass blowers at work. A goblet classed as a second, which may have minute flaws, sells for about $10.00 at the seconds price. The quantities are there. You can buy a whole set or just a few pieces.

# Restaurant Supply Stores

## COMMERCIAL FOOD EQUIPMENT CO.
501 E. 12th St., Oakland. Phone: 893-2736. Hours: M-F 8:30 am-5pm. Purchases: Cash, check. Parking: Street.

Restaurant supply stores are truly a boon for families with fumbly-fingered young children (or couples who fight a lot).

A magnificent assortment of sturdy dishes is available in the back room of this establishment. While restaurant dishes may not have the graceful look of your regular china, they will probably last a lot longer. Both new and used dishes are priced by the dozen here; for quantities of less than a dozen, 10% is added to the price. On used dishes, savings are about 50%, and all they need is a little soap and water to become useful additions to your kitchen.

## FOOD SERVICE EQUIPMENT INC.
710 E. 14th St., San Leandro. Phone: 568-2922. Hours: M-F 8am-5pm, Sat 9am-2pm. Purchases: BA, MC. Parking: Street.

This is the nicest restaurant supply store I've found so far. It's spacious and attractive, with merchandise beautifully displayed. On the main floor there are always specials on discontinued merchandise, with many one-of-a-kind items. The upstairs back room is stacked high with sturdy restaurant dishes in many colors and patterns (or plain, even). Here there are used dishes and kitchenware at savings of about 50%, discontinued lines of dishes, and new dishes that have been returned to the store. Dishes are priced by the dozen.

# Draperies
## Fabrics

(Also see **Fabrics—Drapery and Upholstery Yardage and Supplies**)

## Ready Made

### AMERICAN DRAPERIES
2466 American Ave. (of Clawiter), Hayward 94545. Phone: 783-5551. Hours: Announced in Bay Area Newspapers. Purchases: BA, MC.

*American Draperies* makes draperies for homes and apartment houses. Twice a year they clear out their warehouse of miscellaneous stock, discontinued fabrics, production overruns, and odd sizes, all priced between $9.00 and $23.00. Bring your rod sizes and lengths required. The draperies are on hangers in panels or pairs. The fabrics are sold for 39¢-99¢/yard. There are hundreds of roll ends and bundles of assorted fabrics at 50¢ per bundle. Their sales are announced in Bay Area newspapers and usually occur in May and November. All sales are final. For the best selection be there when the doors open; however, at 2:30 in the afternoon, an additional 20% discount is applied to the sale merchandise.

### CUSTOMADES DRAPERY CO.
Fremont Fashion Plaza, 39220 Paseo Padre Pkwy, Fremont. Phone: 792-0231. Hours: MWTh 9:30am-9pm, TFSat 9:30-5:30pm. Purchases: BA, MC.

Other Stores: San Leandro, Walnut Creek, Antioch, Pleasanton.

*Customades* stocks custom-quality draperies made for standard size windows priced well below most other stores. For an additional charge drapes can be made up to the customer's measure. The reduced price comes from the customer's willingness to provide their own measures, arrange their own installation and use fabrics that will not be in stock six months later. The expensive part of custom drapery is the fabric. These fabrics are excellent custom fabrics but are purchased by *Customades* at reduced prices because they are either closeouts, surplus, etc. Their ready-mades are an expedient choice for the lady decorating in a hurry.

### FOOTHILL DRAPERIES
897 Blossom Hill Rd. & Pearl (Oakridge Mall), San Jose. Phone: 226-4262. Hours: M-Sat 9:30am-9:30pm, Sun 10am-6pm. Purchases: BA, MC. Parking: Lot.

Other Stores: Santa Clara, San Jose (Lo Bue Center).

This custom drapery store has found a way to cut losses and keep their overhead down. They utilize all leftover fabrics by making up ready-made draperies in standard window sizes. They have about 1,000 of these leftovers in their three showrooms. Most are one-of-a-kind and there are some customer returns. You can buy custom quality at 30-40% off. Bring your measurements and choose from satins, brocades, open weaves, linens, patterns and sheers.

### THE YARDSTICK
2110 S. Bascom Ave., Campbell 95008. Phone: 377-1401. Purchases: BA, MC. Parking: Lot.

If you need draperies right away or you want luxury window treatments at budget prices, check the mezzanine at *The Yardstick.* They usually have about 1,000 ready-mades (guaranteed 2½ fullness) from their own workrooms ready for you to take home and hang. Bring your measurements and in no time at all you'll be walking out the door with your selections. The fabrics used in their draperies are suitable for windows in a cabin or at the other extreme, in a formal dining room. *The Yardstick* always has "specials" for the seamstress. Check their ads in the San Jose "Mercury" for your dress, drapery, or upholstery needs. Pass up those high prices on notions by checking their low prices and selection of closeouts on buttons, zippers, buckles, and trims.

## Custom Draperies

### WESTERN CONTRACT FURNISHERS
(See **Furniture and Accessories—Catalog Discounters**)

# Eyeglasses and Frames

## FOR EYES
610 Sacramento, San Francisco. Phone: 421-6250. Hours: M-Sat 10am-6pm. Parking: Pay Garage, Street. Purchase: Cash, check.

Other Stores: 2500 Telegraph, Berkeley.

If you have a friend who just bought a new pair of glasses don't tell them about *For Eyes,* you'll only make them unhappy. This company was started five years ago on the East Coast by a group of consumer oriented opticians from Philadelphia. Since then the company has grown and now boasts its own processing lab and 20 shops operating across the country which gives them considerable volume buying power. The primary goal of *For Eyes* is providing the highest possible quality for the lowest possible price. The standard price for single vision glasses is $29. which includes frame, lenses, and tinting, even for photochromatic lenses. Glass bifocals with frames and tinting cost $35, while plastic or photogrey bifocals are $45. This is not a bait and switch operation, there are over 400 frames in the selection for men, women and children. Rimless and designer frames are available at slightly higher prices. Delivery time is normally ten days to two weeks.

An important consideration is their guarantee. All frames are guaranteed against defects for one year. The lenses are made by the same reliable companies that are used by other dispensing offices and stores. They are guaranteed to be filled according to the Doctors prescription. If any mistakes occur, they will be replaced free of charge. Adjustments are free at any time. The *For Eyes* concept is long overdue in the Bay Area for people on fixed incomes or tight budgets. Others, less budget minded, will feel euphoric at the prospect of buying three pairs of fashionable glasses for the price of one elsewhere.

# Fabrics
## General

### CAPWELL'S BUDGET STORE
(See **Family Clothing**)

### THE ELEGANT COAT & DRESS OUTLET
(See **Women's Clothing**)

### EMERYVILLE CLOTHING AND FABRIC OUTLET
(See **Women's Clothing**)

### FABRIANO FABRICS
2005 San Pablo Ave., Berkeley. Phone: 849-3460. Hours: M-Sat 9am-5:30pm. Purchases: BA, MC.

The owner of this store was quite reluctant to share his buying secrets with me (he obviously thought I was a spy from a competitor). Anyone who sews would recognize his great prices. There are tables heaped full of fabrics, apparently leftovers from Eastern textile mills. All are first quality, and usually marked 40-60% off.

I could hardly restrain myself from scooping up zippers to last a lifetime of sewing. Name-brand zippers are sold, removed from their packages, for mere pennies. The more you buy, the cheaper they are. Go bananas over the buttons and large spools of threads from manufacturers' sewing rooms. There are good-quality upholstery shorts—buy two or three matching pieces and you've got enough to cover a chair. Watch for his ads in the Oakland "Tribune" or "Classified Flea Market" for his frequent special purchases that represent super buys. None of the fabrics are labeled, so you'll have to resort to the old rub-a-dub-dub test.

## FACTORY STORE
(See **Women's Clothing**)

## HARAN'S
408 No. Capitol Ave., San Jose. Phone: 923-9887. Hours: M-Sat 9am-5:30pm, Sun Noon-5pm. Purchases: BA, MC. Parking: Free Lot.

Other Stores: Redwood City, San Francisco, San Jose.

*Haran's* offers all kinds of fabrics at fantastically reduced prices—some fabrics here are for sale elsewhere at twice the price. There are cottons from 69¢ a yard, acetates at $1 a yard, and drapery and upholstery fabrics at $1.98 a yard. Almost everything in the store is specially purchased from mills in other states. Good buys are plentiful here, but be alert for second-quality merchandise; check the fabric for flaws before purchasing. This store will make exchanges, but you will save time if you're careful before you buy.

## IMPORO
149 10th Street (upstairs), San Francisco. Phone: 552-0132. Hours: M-Sat 9am-50m. Parking: Street. Purchases: Cash, check.

Located next to the *Jonathon Logan Fabric Warehouse*, *Imporo* offers a wide selection of pre-cut fabrics at bargain hunters prices. There are many synthetics and natural fibers (including wools) that make sewing your own clothes a real money saver. They are also selling some ladies clothing which are manufacturers overruns at rock bottom prices.

## LINGERIE FABRIC OUTLET

1047 Elwell Court, Palo Alto. Phone: 965-1550. Hours: M-F 8am-4:30pm. Purchases: Cash, check. Parking: Street, Lot.

There are several businesses in this commercial building, you have to pass about six doorways down the side of the building to get to the outlet. Fabrics from their sewing rooms, velours, jerseys, terry cloth, lingerie fabrics and trims etc. are sold in pieces, (not off the roll) at wholesale prices. They always have 4-5 racks of garments from their line of fancy lingerie which includes slips, camisoles, panties, robes, hostess pajamas, elegant and Tom-Boy type sleepwear and coverups. These irregulars and samples are priced about 50% off retail. The selection is small but choice—especially if you can stop by frequently to skim through the racks. Fortunately, there is one little dressing room.

## KORET CLOTHING OUTLET
(See **Women's Clothing**)

## REDWOOD CITY KNITTING MILLS AND FABRIC OUTLET
(See **Women's Clothing**)

# Drapery and Upholstery Yardage and Supplies

(Also see **Furniture and Accessories—Catalog Discounters; Draperies—Ready Made**)

## ALAMEDA UPHOLSTERY SHOP

863 W. San Carlos, San Jose 95126. Phone: 295-7885. Hours: M-F 9am-5:30pm, Sat 9am-4pm. Purchases: BA, MC. Parking: Street.

Whether you need supplies for reupholstering a piece of furniture or just advice about doing it, this shop can help you. They cater to do-it-yourselfers, with some nice fringe benefits. For example, they make up a small beginners' kit that includes most of the tools needed to start reupholstering on your own, and they usually have a few books on the subject as well. Their selection of upholstery fabrics is huge, and they can order from almost any major manufacturer in the country, including Van Waters & Rogers, Schumaker, Bird, and many others at savings of 10% to 25%. (Students can get another 10% discount.) The proprietors are two brothers who have been in this business for many years and are willing to take time to help even the rankest amateur.

## CALICO CORNERS

2727 El Camino Real, Redwood City 94061. Phone: 364-1610. Hours: M-Sat 9:30am-5:30pm. Purchases: BA, MC. Parking: Free Lot.

Other Store: 5753 Pacheco Blvd., Pacheco.

The real bargains are not calico, actually, but beautiful imported and domestic upholstery fabrics—some of the finest upholstery fabrics, drapery, and slipcover fabrics I have seen, for 50% off regular retail price. Hanging rolls neatly display beautiful fabrics whose only fault are tiny minute flaws that can easily be worked around (some weren't even visible to the unprofessional eye). Each piece is tagged with fiber content, width, price, and place of manufacture. This store is an absolute pleasure to shop in, not only for its extraordinarily low prices, but also for its neat arrangement and its helpful clerks, who will refer you to a custom upholsterer on request.

### DISCOUNT WALLPAPER
(See **Wallpaper**)

### WALL COVERINGS UNLIMITED
(See **Wallpaper**)

# Flowers, Plants, Pots

(Also see **General Merchandise—Discount Stores**)

## General

### AMLING FLOWERS
3379 El Camino Real, Santa Clara 95051. Phone: 246-8676. Hours: M-Sat 9:30am-6pm; Sun 11am-5pm. Purchases: BA, MC. Parking: Free lot.

Supplies for all amateur (and even professional) flower arrangers can be purchased here at 10% less than at a retail florist's. The prices are not always the lowest to be found, but this is one of the few places where you can regularly purchase fresh flowers (large bunches) at a discount. Dried flowers cost much less here than at a department store, too. They have all shapes and sizes of baskets, candles, and glass and plastic flower holders. This is a self-service store. Take a cart when you go in; the place is big, and you'll be glad you did. Clerks are more than willing to help or to offer suggestions.

### ARCHITECTURAL CERAMICS
1940 Union Street, Oakland (1½ blocks off Grand Ave.). Phone: 893-5314. Hours: Sales announced by newspaper or mailing list. Purchases: Cash, check. Parking: Street.

Periodically this manufacturer becomes overstocked with seconds in the large ceramic plant containers and crocks they manufacture. Their pots are usually seen accommodating large plants and indoor trees in lobbys and office buildings. Held without any fanfare their sales occur on Saturdays and Sundays from 9:00am-6pm. You can get on their mailing list for sale announcements by giving them a call. Then be there early to take advantage of the 50-65% savings. Sale prices on these pots range from $4.00-$25.00 depending on the flaws in the glaze or size of the chip.

## FANTASTICO
(See **Arts, Crafts, Hobby Supplies**)

## FLOWER TERMINAL
6th and Brannan, San Francisco. Hours: M-F 2am-11am. Purchases: Cash or check.

Several wholesale nurseries are located within this block of buildings. Retail sales of house plants are made to the public at wholesale prices. Because these businesses are basically wholesale operations, this is certainly not the place to shop with your children or to expect information on plant maintenance or other advice. The quick cash sale is appreciated but there is neither time nor personnel for retail services. You are required to pay sales tax unless you have a resale number. Only people with resale numbers are allowed to park within their lot and street parking can be a real problem! For the best service and selection I recommend shopping on Tuesdays and Thursdays.

## PAYLESS DRUG STORE'S GARDEN CENTERS
2130 Contra Costa Blvd., Pleasant Hill 94523. Phone: 685-2450. Hours: M-F 9:30am-9pm; Sat 9am-8pm; Sun 9am-7pm. Purchases: Cash, check, BA, MC. Parking: Free lot.

Other Stores: Castro Valley, Dublin, Fremont, Hayward, Oakland, San Mateo, San Pablo, San Rafael, Santa Rosa, Vallejo.

For garden plants it's hard to find better prices than the ones at *Payless Drug Store's Garden Centers.* Their secret is volume buying and quick turnover. Each store does its own buying to suit the special climatic and soil conditions of its area. Since this is a self-service store, you won't get the attention you might get at a nursery.

Prices are as much as 50% below those of independent nurseries during their seasonal sales. Usually garden department sales are held every three weeks throughout the year; these are advertised in local papers. During spring and fall, the peak gardening seasons, sales occur weekly. Even without the sales, prices are 25-35% less than you'll find almost anywhere else.

*Payless* will accept exchanges on plants that do not thrive or aren't satisfactory if you have your sales slip (otherwise at the discretion of the garden center manager).

### PLANT OUTLET
24949 Soto Road, Hayward 94544. Phone: 415-886-1577. Hours: Tues-Sat 11am-5pm, Sun 11am-4pm. Purchases: MC, BA.

*The Plant Outlet* was previously a wholesale growing operation that decided to deal directly with the public. The results are gratifying for all concerned. The best buys and largest selection are in the hanging plant categories: ferns, creeping charlies, piggybacks, spider plants, etc. The uprights, palms, philodendrums, ficus trees etc., are available in good quantity and at good prices. There are thousands of plants under the roof of this huge growing shed and I've never seen anyone leave with just one plant. At their prices you can't resist buying three or four. In all my travels I haven't found another place that offers such low prices for such huge plants! It's very nice too, to deal with a grower who has so many helpful employees to give advice and help you with your selection. Customers are appreciated at *The Plant Outlet!*

### SUNOL NURSERIES
1000 Calaveras Rd. (at Hwy. 680), Sunol 94586. Phone: 862-2286. Hours: Daily 8am-4:30pm. Purchases: BA, MC. Parking: Free lot.

Take a ride out to the country, not only for fun but for the money you can save here. *Sunol Nurseries* is a wholesale nursery open to the public. Bud Martin, the owner, and his men are congenial and willing to help and will give you detailed landscaping instructions. Take your landscaping plans with you to make it easier when you get there, and pick up a catalog when you are there—it describes and illustrates most of the plants and shrubs they sell, with some planting instruction. No catalogs will be sent by mail. There is a very helpful price guide with the retail price listed next to the wholesale price. You can get further discounts, if, or when, you buy in lots of 5, 10, or 25 plants. "Sunset" garden books are 20% less, too.

# Christmas Tree Farms

Each year the children excitedly look forward to our seasonal excursion to a choose-and-cut Christmas tree farm. Most Christmas tree farms, which usually open the first weekend after Thanksgiving, can be reached in less than an hour's drive. At the farm you are provided with a saw, and you strike out on your own—in some cases over rather rough terrain. At this time of year the weather may be wet or cold, which is why smart people wear warm clothing and sturdy shoes. You may need to muster the combined strength of the whole family to carry a 15-foot tree a half mile back to the car.

But besides the exhilaration and general fun of the outing, you also save a good deal of money. We have never bought a tree less than 10 feet tall and have never spent more than $9. Some growers charge by the foot, but most charge a flat rate per tree, regardless of size (usually less than $10).

Many varieties are available, primarily the Monterey pine (which most growers shear as the trees mature for a full bushy conformation). You may also find Douglas firs,

Incense cedars, Sierra redwoods, Scotch pines, and others. Your tree will be as fresh as you can get, and will last much longer than one bought off a lot at home. (The Christmas Tree Association advises you to keep your tree outside with the trunk immersed in water until you're ready to use it. After the tree is inside, sprinkle water on the branches occasionally to retain freshness.)

To receive a listing of Northern California choose-and-cut Christmas Tree farms, write to the California Christmas Tree Growers at 2855 Telegraph Ave., Berkeley 94705.

# Food and Drink

(Also see **General Merchandise—Discount Stores, —Liquidators**)

## Bakery Thrift Shops

There is a large assortment of bakery goods available in San Francisco and the rest of the Bay Area at low, low prices if you're willing to make the trip to one of the outlets (not a long trip, because there are bakery thrift shops turning up all over the place). The Oroweat, Langendorf, and Kilpatrick baking companies have thrift stores throughout the Bay Area where you can buy either day-old bread at about 50% off regular retail prices or freshly-baked (surplus) goods for about 20% off. Save on the purchase of cakes, cookies, donuts, and sweet rolls, too. Buy a lot at one time—you can freeze whatever you don't use right away.

## Groceries

**AKRON**
(See **General Merchandise—Discount Stores—Liquidators**)

**CANNED FOODS, INC.**
54 Dory St. (intercepts Folsom between 10th and 11th), San Francisco. Phone: 861-5986. Hours: M-F 10am-8pm, Sat 8am-7pm, Sun 9am-6pm. Purchases: Cash, check. Parking: Free lot.

Other Stores: Berkeley, Castro Valley, Redwood City, San Francisco.

Today's high food prices make everyone a potential fan of *Canned Food, Inc.* There you'll see row upon row of canned goods in cutaway cases, stacked 6 to 8 feet high, at savings of as much as 40%.

The goods are warehouse damaged or downgraded, closeouts, or from an odd lot. For the protection of customers and the name-brand suppliers, stringent and thorough quality control is exercised. Cans are carefully examined, and torn packages and severely dented cans (in the rim of seams) are discarded. All merchandise is guaranteed. Although some of the cans are dented, the labels are familiar and the quality is as high as in your supermarket.

As a supplement to their salvage merchandise they also sell meat, staple goods, and toiletries at no more than supermarket prices.

They have a wide selection of restaurant-size canned goods, especially useful for big families and group events.

## CANNED FOODS WAREHOUSE
## DISTRIBUTION CENTER

14th & Harrison, San Francisco. Phone: 961-1495. Hours: M-Sat 9am-5pm. Purchases: Check, cash.

A new division of *Canned Food,* the distribution center is limited to case sales only. It's a real boon to institutions and restaurants, but there is also potential for the price-conscious homemaker. Stock up as a hedge against inflation and save from 20-50% on many case sales. Other items such as candy, paper goods, dog food, and cans in institutional sizes are available. Many items are relabeled products from national manufacturers. Other special prices are due to closeouts, carload purchases, warehouse and transportation damage. Everything is guaranteed! Cases of canned goods too much for your family??? Come in with 2 or 3 of your friends and purchase jointly to get the quantity you want at these great savings!

## CITTADEL'S CANNERY WAREHOUSE

East Taylor (between 9th & 10th), San Jose 95112. Phone: 275-0410. Hours: M-Sat 10am-6pm, Sun noon-5pm. Purchases: Cash, check. Parking: Street.

The selection of dented cans and odd lots for sale here (by the case or half case) covers the whole warehouse floor. You take a list as you enter, then check off your choices as you walk through; the cases or half cases are picked up for you while you wait at the front. They charge 25¢ extra for cutting cases, but the buys are still good enough to make your trip here worthwhile. Prices on canned goods are usually at least 30% less than retail. Both institutional and regular sizes are available, but not every size in every weight. There are many nationally known brands for sale, along with *Cittadel's* own brand. The quality of all items is guaranteed. You should shop here early in the morning on a weekday, since the afternoons and Saturdays are fairly busy. Save money by shopping with friends and splitting cases.

## CO-OP SUPERMARKETS
## (Consumers Cooperative of Berkeley, Inc.)

1414 University Ave., Berkeley 94702. Phone: 848-6001. Hours: M-F 9:30am-8pm, Sat 9am-8pm, Sun 10am-7pm. Purchase: Cash, check. Parking: Free lot.

Other Stores: Berkeley, Castro Valley, Corte Madera, El Cerrito, Oakland, Walnut Creek.

If you can't face grocery shopping with any enthusiasm, you probably haven't discovered the *Co-op Supermarkets.* You'll be delighted by all their little extras—the Kiddie Korral for little tots, the paperback book exchange, home economists who can answer questions and give advice, and the community and swap-shop bulletin boards.

The *Co-op* is owned by the 90,000 member families. Together they own the business; they're buying from their own organization. The best bargain is having a voice in the policy and operation of the business, which is a real education. You can shop in the market even if you are not a *Co-op* member; if you want to be a member-owner after investigating the store and other services, then join. Shares are $5 each; every member has a vote in the organization.

Not only are the grocery prices competitive with other stores', but you'll also have these added features when shopping at the *Co-op:* bargain-priced *Co-op* label products (detergent, paper goods, canned foods, pastas), kosher foods, Oriental products, El Molino flours and cereals, and other hard-to-find imported foods. There are informative newsletters, consumer education displays, suggestion boxes, a library of *Co-op* literature, and other *Co-op* sponsored activities such as pre-schools and baby-sitting exchanges. The most popular *Co-op* services include the credit union, health plan, legal services, Camp Sierra, and travel service.

## HOOPERS CHOCOLATES AND GIFTS

4632 Telegraph Ave., Oakland 94609. Phone: 654-3373. Hours: M-Sat 9:30am-6pm. Purchases: BA, MC. Parking: Street.

Just because you don't see their seconds, don't think they're not here. Just ask and they'll sell you whatever they have on hand in their stock room. Regularly priced at $3.00, the seconds in chews and creams are just $1.98 a pound. Candy seconds at *Hoopers* may be irregularly shaped or lacking in gloss, or that little squiggle on top may be messy instead of artistic. One thing for sure, they still taste good. You have to buy a 50¢ minimum, but that's not hard as you contemplate rum, maple, almond, raspberry, or chocolate creams, or how about walnut, caramel, coffee, or almond nugget chews? Deeee-licious!!!

## OLD WORLD CHEESE COMPANY

107 Monument Plaza, Pleasant Hill. Phone: 798-9107. Hours: Daily 9am-5pm. Purchases: Cash, check, food stamps. Parking: Street.

Rather barnlike in appearance, the customers seem to appreciate the savings more than the decor. This is where I stock up on cheeses and other goodies for my pantry. For cheese priced low in bulk 5-10# packages, I simply cut them into one pound blocks and freeze.

Cheese will keep up to three months in the freezer. Mozzarella at $1.39/pound is quite a savings from Safeway's $1.95/pound. Bulk pastas, cases of canned goods and other bulk grocery items are bargain priced. One item that I've found a lifesaver is their fresh pizza crusts which are $1.95 for five large, and $1.49 for five small ones. Spread with sauce and cheese—they're ready for the oven.

## SODA POP STOP

970 S. Bascom Ave., San Jose 95128. Phone: 294-0666. Hours: M-Th 10am-6pm, F-Sat 10am-7pm, Sun 11am-5pm. Purchases: BA, MC.

If you like really exotic flavors in soda pop you'll have no trouble finding them here. Cases are stacked 6 feet high. Your savings are made possible by purchasing your favorite beverages by the case. You can choose cases in cans, non-returnable bottles, or returnable bottles in all flavors and brands in diet or regular. Of course, the biggest savings are on returnable bottles. The owners take advantage of special manufacturers' promotional sales and price rollbacks, and then pass the savings on to you. Comparison shoppers are guided by their special unit pricing signs, which reflect the price advantage of case sales over individual or 6-pack prices.

# Produce

### FARMERS MARKET ARCADE
100 Alemany Blvd., San Francisco 94110. Phone: 826-9821. Hours: M-F 9am-5pm, Sat 8am-5pm. Purchases: Cash only. Parking: Free lot.

There is something about open-air markets and fresh produce that appeals to everyone. *The Farmers Market,* where smaller farmers come to sell their produce direct to you, is a very enjoyable place to shop. The prices are reasonable, and you can count on freshness. This marketplace has been here a long time; many people have been customers for years. The thirty or so stalls are arranged side by side, with a small overhanging roof in case of rain. I suggest checking out the produce at each stand and noting prices before deciding just what to buy. Many of the vendors are real characters. (I noticed that some of the sellers are quite willing to let you sample before you buy, but ominous signs above other stalls read "NO TASTING.") Shop early because it gets quite crowded after 11am.

### GOLDEN GATE PRODUCE TERMINAL
Produce Ave., South San Francisco. Hours: M-F 1:30am-10am.

Just look for the long row of buildings and then try to find a parking place. Although they will do business with co-ops, you'll not find the service of your friendly neighborhood grocery store.

### OAKLAND PRODUCE MART
Dealers located at 2nd & Franklin (near Jack London Square), Oakland. Hours: M-F 1:30am-approx. 11am. Purchases: Cash, check. Parking: Street.

The Oakland Produce Mart handles 90% of the produce sold by independent retailers in the East Bay. The 15 wholesalers buy and sell from a cavernous open stall divided by high wooden walls and floor-to-ceiling wire mesh. They start work about 1:30am, trading peaks early in the morning, and they begin to close at 11am. For housewives seeking escape from high retail food costs, this source is about the best way I know to save money on vegetables, fruit, beans, rice, even peanuts. All the produce is sold by the crate, dozen, or sack.

Co-op shoppers are welcome, as well as individuals willing to buy in bulk quantities. The sellers at the Produce Mart prefer selling to the public during the middle of the week. On Mondays, Fridays, and days before and after holidays, they're just too busy.

This is one of the few business left that operates by supply and demand. Prices vary according to the quality and kind of food, time of day, and how well the sales are going. You can usually count on saving at least 25-50%.

Starting a co-op is not difficult and it behooves every bargain hunter to consider the effort and try to round up friends and neighbors to share in the benefits of co-op shopping.

My co-op has 12 member families. Every two weeks, two members take our grocery list and "do the shopping." We prefer getting there early in the morning (around 6:30am). We can usually make our selections, have our wagon loaded, and be back home by 7:30am, just in time to get everybody off to school. I don't mind the early hours because my turn comes only once every three months. Occasionally I'll buy a crate of asparagus or favorite fruit for myself and put it all in my freezer. How nice to have asparagus for months instead of weeks!

### SAN FRANCISCO PRODUCE TERMINAL
2000 block of Jerrold Ave., San Francisco. Hours: 1:30am-9:30am.

This large complex is overwhelming with its high loading docks and vast selection of produce. When I went to shop I felt very insignificant moving around between huge trucks and busy busy men.

# Produce "Down on the Farm"

If you're really feeling the pinch of high food costs, try saving money by going to the source—the grower—and eliminating all those middleman expenses in between. Many farmers and ranchers seasonally set up fruit stands on or near their farms and sell to the public. You benefit in two ways: first, you'll save money; second, you'll be buying

really fresh, farm-ripened, flavorful produce. It's well worth the drive into the country, especially if you buy in quantity or if you have a talent for home canning. Some farmers invite people to pick their own for even greater savings.

Many farms do not advertise, but the word is spread by satisfied customers who return year after year during the harvest season. The San Jose "Mercury" and San Jose "News" have a classified section entitled "Good Things to Eat," with listings of local growers.

Following is a list of Growers' Associations who print brochures complete with maps pinpointing the growers who sell to the public, the foods they harvest and harvest times. Send a *self-addressed stamped envelope* to the addresses below to get a copy, then plan your summer excursions.

*Contra Costa County:*
### HARVEST TIME
P. O. Box 0
Brentwood, Ca 94513

*Eldorado County:*
### APPLE HILL GROWERS
P. O. Box 494
Camino, Ca 95709

*Sonoma County:*
### SONOMA COUNTY FARM TRAILS
P. O. Box 6043
Santa Rosa, Ca 95406

*Yolo and Solano Counties:*
**YOLANO HARVEST TRAILS**
P. O. Box 484
Winters, Ca 95694

# Furniture and Accessories
## General

### A. C. GRAPHICS
79 Belevedere Street #12 (1 block East Francisco Blvd.)
San Rafael 94902. Phone: 456-0363. Hours: M-F 9am-5pm,
Sat 9am-2pm. Purchase: Cash, check. Parking: Street.

Seconds on stretched handscreened printed cotton graphics are ½ the wholesale price. These fine graphics are frequently seen on walls in lobbies and business offices around the Bay. You can buy one or combine two or more to fill a wide expanse of bare wall. They also sell 2nds and 3rds of fabric for you do-it-yourselfers at prices that are hard to beat anywhere. Many quilt makers find *A. C. Graphic's* quality fabrics and prices easy on the wallet. *A. C.* has a space in an industrial complex so be sure to look for door #12 down the side of the building.

### ABBEY RENTS . . . AND SELLS
1314 Post St., San Francisco 94109. Phone: 771-3700.
Hours: M-F 8am-5pm, Sat 8am-1pm. Purchases: BA, MC.
Parking: Street.

Other Stores: Hayward, Oakland, Santa Clara, San Mateo.

We all think of *Abbey Rents* as the best-known renter of all kinds of furniture and equipment. However, are you aware that they have a new name, "Abbey Rents . . . and Sells," and that the same merchandise is also for sale at any one of the stores in the Bay Area? Periodically, certain goods are judged obsolete and put on special sale at each office-warehouse. You can buy furniture, party paraphernalia, sickroom equipment, and reducing gear. The condition of these items ranges from slightly to very used, with prices corresponding. Most are reduced about 40-60% from their original price at the discretion of each individual manager. Occasionally sales are announced in the local papers, but it's best to call and inquire at the store nearest you.

### BRUENERS CLEARANCE CENTER
1600 Duane Ave., Santa Clara. Phone: 408-378-9400.
Hours: MTSat 10am-5pm, WThF 10am-9pm, Sun noon-5pm. Purchases: BA, MC, Store charge. Parking: Lot.

Other Store: 100 Admiral Callaghan Lane (off Fwy 80), Vallejo.

A large selection of left-overs, floor samples, discontinued, cancelled orders, slightly damaged or distressed furniture pieces from *Brueners* retail stores, are offered here at outlet prices, 30-50% off. There are great values in furniture, carpet remnants, dinettes, bedroom sets, mattresses, and a few accessory items. Each item is tagged with the original price and the as-is clearance price. Delivery is extra and varies according to the size of the item and delivery distance. You may go around in circles trying to find this outlet which is located right next to Fwy. 101, off the San Tomas Expressway.

## BUS VAN
900 Battery St., San Francisco 94111. Phone: 981-1405. Hours: M-F 9:30am-6pm, Sat 10am-5:30pm, Sun noon-6pm. Purchases: BA, MC. Parking: Pay lot, off street.

Other Stores: San Francisco, 244 Clement.

If you are on a low budget, or trying to furnish a vacation home at bargain prices, *Bus Van* offers real possibilities. Almost anything can be purchased from their three-story warehouse: furniture, appliances, rugs, pianos, antiques, paintings, books, bric-a-brac, and office furniture. The ground floor features used furniture at rock-bottom prices—this comes from unclaimed storage, estate sales, or purchase from private parties. The selection is always changing; it pays to stop by often.

The third floor features new budget-priced and moderate-priced furniture at substantial savings over retail prices. All sales are final. A 20% deposit will hold merchandise for 30 days. Bring your own station wagon or van, since the minimum delivery charge is $19.50.

## CALIFORNIA FURNITURE SALES
3549 El Camino Real, Santa Clara 95051. Phone: 243-6440. Hours: M-Sat 10am-6pm. Purchases: MC, BA. Parking: Street.

If you don't have time to scout the garage sales, this is the place to go for budget-priced home furnishings. This furniture rental company always has a good selection of used furniture. Some pieces, wellll—you know they've been used—but they're still usable, and sofas for $50-$150 are good values. Then there are many pieces that were on display in apartment or condominium models. They look like new but truly can't be sold as new furniture or for new prices. You'll save 20-40%. The styles go right down the middle, conventional or traditional—the type that appeals to the majority of people. You can also pick up tables, chairs, lamps, pictures, mattresses, bedroom and dining sets, and accessories. Check their prices on the new furniture too . . . I saw some good buys. Delivery is free on purchases over $200 in Santa Clara County.

## CAPTAINS CUSHIONS
255 4th St., Oakland. Phone: 832-0738. Hours: T-F 10am-5:30pm. Purchases: Cash, check. Parking: Street.

Other Stores: San Jose Flea Market on Weekends.

This little factory is a real mom-and-pop operation. In fact, you can watch them at work while you rummage through the intriguing assortment of cushions and pillows. You can outfit every room in your house with the selection of pillows in a wide variety of fabrics sold here. There are cushions suitable for the family room, bedrooms, campers, and cabins. You may be tempted to take a flying leap into a passion pouf—but once deposited you will find it hard to leave your cozy nest. The prices will fit even the most modest budget, ranging from $4-35 for a large pouf. Lots of fake furs are used in the poufs and it's possible to buy a fur waterbed bedspread at a price that puts the waterbed store prices to shame! *Captains Cushions* also rents a stall at the San Jose Flea Market every weekend. Catch them there!

## CAPWELL'S CLEARANCE CENTER
1 El Cerrito Plaza, El Cerrito 94530. Phone: 526-1111. Hours: M-F noon-9pm, Sat 9:30am-6pm, Sun noon-5pm. Purchases: Cash, check, store charge. Parking: Free lot.

Here, on the third floor of the El Cerrito store, is the last-post outlet for furniture from all the *Capwell's* stores. The savings are really spectacular—there are great values in furniture, rugs, carpets, dinettes, small and major appliances, draperies, bedroom sets, mattresses, lamps, pictures, household items, and even linens and bedding (mostly seconds and irregulars on the latter). Save 20-50% on discontinued styles, floor samples, and slightly damaged goods, all of which were once offered at regular retail prices. All "as is" sales are final. You may use your store charge on any of these purchases; if you're willing to take delivery of furniture yourself, you'll get an additional discount.

## EMPORIUM FURNITURE CLEARANCE CENTER
5353 Almaden Expressway, Almaden Fashion Plaza, San Jose. Phone: 265-1111. Hours: M-F 12am-9pm, Sat 10am-6pm, Sun 12am-5pm. Purchases: Cash, check. Parking: Free Lot.

Here, on the third floor, they collect all the floor samples, discontinued pieces, slightly damaged and soiled items, and one-of-a-kind pieces from the various *Emporium* stores in the Bay Area. Choose from sofas, mattresses, carpets, stereos, and appliances, sold at 20-50% off. There is also a small selection of towels (mostly seconds or irregulars), housewares (some slightly damaged but still usable), and drapes. Of course, all sales are final.

## FOSS ANNEX
1326 E. 12th St., Oakland. Phone: 534-4133. Hours: M-F 9:30am-5pm. Purchases: Cash, check. Parking: Street.

*The Foss Annex* is located right next to the Foss Factory, a company that has been in business for 50 years making some of the finest lampshades you can buy. Their customers are usually interior decorators (shopping for their clients), hotels, restaurants, and prestige home furnishing stores. They've been entrusted with the job of restoring and replacing shades for places as famous as the Hearst Castle.

Occasionally something goes wrong in the factory; an imperfection in fabric, finishing, construction, or patterns becomes evident on the final inspection. These "misfits" are sent to the annex, where less fickle people like you or me will delight at marked-down prices. Since all Foss shades are handmade, even outlet prices may seem high until you consider the level of craftsmanship and original pricing. You can spend from $6 to $50. Be sure to bring your lamp in with you (you wouldn't buy a hat without trying it on). On floor lamps just bring in the measurements of the reflector bowl. Pick up a simple basic shade, then jazz it up with some of their trims. The trims alone are worth a trip—a 50 year collection of discontinued trims at give-away prices!

## FURNITURE CLEARANCE CENTER

317 "B" St., San Mateo. Phone: 347-1241. Hours: M-F 10am-9pm, Sat 10am-5:30pm, Sun noon-5pm. Purchases: BA, MC, VISA. Parking: Free lot.

Other Stores: San Francisco, San Jose.

The final destination of discontinued or floor sample merchandise from the W.&J. Sloane furniture stores is one of their *Furniture Clearance Centers.* All furniture is representative of the fine quality available in Sloane stores; savings may range up to 60%.

A huge showroom boasts extensive selections in living room, dining room, and bedroom furniture, many unusual accessories, carpeting, and occasional specials on items like bedspreads. The Furniture Clearance Center also makes special purchases, either from outside manufacturers or from display furniture at the Furniture Mart or Ice House, to maintain a constant selection in the showrooms.

It is worthwhile to stop in frequently because the selection is always changing; prices are lowered frequently on some articles to move them faster.

Regular store services, such as credit, are not available. All sales are final. No returns or exchanges are accepted. Delivery can be arranged.

## GRANTREE FURNITURE RENTALS

3600 Stevens Creek Blvd., San Jose 95117. Phone: 249-2410. Hours: M-F 10am-9pm, Sat 10am-6pm, Sun 11am-5pm. Purchases: BA, MC. Parking: Free lot.

This large showroom disposes of rental furniture. All items available are on display; there is no back stock. While some items are seriously damaged, others have only slight imperfections and make for excellent savings if you consider what they would cost new. Some of the furniture is brand new, mixed in with all of the used. The prices on these new items are fantastic—usually 40% off regular retail. There are very few of these new items on the floor, but this is definitely a place to check for bargains. Another good buy here is the overstock of commercial firm mattresses: a double mattress and box spring can be had for only $69. There are no returns or layaways, so choose carefully. The salesmen are very helpful and will answer any questions they can.

## KING STREET FURNITURE FAIRE

128 King Street, San Francisco 91407. Phone: 495-5907. Hours: M-F 10am-5pm, Sat 10am-6pm, Sun 12am-6pm. Purchases: Cash, check. Parking: Street.

Have you ever wondered what happens to the furniture at manufacturers' and decorators' showrooms like the Furniture Mart, Ice House, or Showcase when its purpose has been served? A lot of it ends up here. This large warehouse store is full of one-of-a-kind, fine quality furnishings—the same furniture you see in those beautiful home furnishings magazine spreads. Because most pieces are unique and high-priced to begin with, the 30-50% savings may still reflect what some would consider a hefty price. There are sofas, chairs, area rugs, wall units, some lamps, graphics, and on the day I stopped in, a preponderance of butcher block tables and bentwood chairs. This is not a typical department store selection of furniture—far from it—and that's precisely what I liked about it. Here's your chance to pick up a really unique piece of furniture. With these price reductions, of course, delivery is extra and all sales are final.

## LAZARUS SALES CO.
(See **Part II—Salvage**)

## MACY'S FURNITURE CLEARANCE PLACE
5160 Stevens Creek Blvd., San Jose 95129. Phone: 248-6343. Hours: M-F 10am-9pm, Sat 9:30am-6pm, Sun noon-5pm. Purchases: Cash, check, Macy's charge. Parking: Lot.

Other Store: San Leandro

*Macy's Furniture Clearance Place* is where you'll find furniture and appliances for 20-40% off. Some pieces are purchased just for *Clearance Place* (budget lines never found in Macy's regular stores); others are buyers' mistakes, distressed or damaged goods, department store overstocks, and discontinued models or lines. You can shop for almost any room in your home for furnishings, appliances, and entertainment needs. Delivery is extra and you'll want to look your selection over carefully, since all sales are final. You can use your Macy's charge account to arrange special terms.

Their linen department, which occupies a space at the back of the store, is where I have found the very best buys in the Bay Area for sheets, towels, comforters, bedspreads, bath rugs etc. When all these discontinued lines, broken lots and leftovers arriver here from the 14 other stores they are priced below cost. By this time Macy's wants them sold and out of their warehouses where space is always in demand. Ann Klein, Halston, Vera, Calvin Klein, Martex, Wamsutta linens are among the fine quality brands sold at these rock bottom, last chance prices. Imagine: a designer king size wheet for $5.99! Often the case during the frequent special sales advertised in the San Jose Mercury.

## NXP
1433 Willow St., Oakland. Phone: 444-1433. Hours: Irregular. Purchases: Cash, check, MC, BA. Parking: Street.

The *NXP* warehouse/showroom is located about a mile SE of the Baybridge Toll Plaza at the corner of 15th Street. The hours are irregular so it's advisable to call ahead and to make sure a salesman will be there to show you the merchandise. I originally purchased a Norsco teak mobile shelf and cabinet system for my family room at approximately ½ of what other wall system stores tried to charge me. As our needs changed I have twice rearranged the system and added new shelving. If you're not too fussy you can buy from the selection of shelving, labeled 2nds, with small flaws that never show once covered with a collection of books and accessories. To make your system complete and also esthetically pleasing you can save about 40-50% on track lighting and other lighting accents for your wall system. Most *NXP* business is done for offices around the Bay Area. The Norsco system is solid, flexible and tops in quality.

## NATIONAL SOFA BED AND MATTRESS CO.

2328 Telegraph Ave., Oakland 94612. Phone: 444-2112. Hours: M-Sat 9am-6pm. Purchases: BA, MC. Parking: Street, free lot.

You'll fine good values in furniture and appliances at *National.* To start with, here is a great way to get a name-brand good-quality mattress at savings up to 60% off. There are usually many slightly irregular factory seconds or mismatched sets to choose from. The defects or flaws are carefully explained to you when you are making a selection. They also have first-quality mattresses, as well as an extensive selection of sofa beds and recliners.

Savings on nationally advertised name-brand recliners and sofa beds range from 15-40%. Although the sales staff is unwilling to discuss their good buys in terms of percentage off retail, I recognized some truly worthwhile savings on this good-quality name-brand furniture. Each piece has two prices, the lowest representing the special value offered by this company. If you have shopped around you you will recognize the savings available. Most sales will include free delivery.

*National* has a complete appliance department including microwaves, and the new video tape recorders (VTR's), all with gratifying discount prices. The final coup for bargain hunters is their fine line of hand-tied sofas and chairs that sell for about the same price as lesser quality production line pieces. These treasures are located in the annex, upstairs behind the main store.

## NIGEL'S

1450 Franklin Street, San Francisco 94109. Phone: 776-5490. Hours: M-F 10am-5:30pm, Sat 10am-4pm. Purchases: BA, MC, VISA. Street: Parking.

It's rather hard to comparison shop imported oriental furniture but I feel *Nigel's* offers far better values, dollar for dollar, than stores selling comparable quality furniture in the Chinatown and downtown areas that cater to the tourist trade. The showroom has a beautiful selection of dining, living, and bedroom furniture, as well as occasional pieces in a choice of natural or dark rosewood. All sofas and chairs are offered in a choice of fabrics. I was particularly impressed that the backs of all the cabinet pieces are finished and need not be pressed up against the wall. I also found the owners to be very knowledgeable and helpful!

## RONEY'S FURNITURE

14000 Washington Ave., San Leandro 94578. Phone: 352-1175. Hours: M-Sat 10am-6pm. Purchases: BA, MC, VISA. Parking: Lot.

Many of my friends will be distressed to see this listing because they've considered *Roney's* "their special place" for years. They will not welcome competition from new buyers over the amazing assortment of freight-damaged merchandise that *Roney* collects direct from local railroad and trucking companies. Although *Roney's* has a little of everything at super bargain prices, I'm most intrigued by his furniture selection. The selection includes low-priced budget lines to topnotch companies. I've seen Ethan Allen pieces on his floor as well as Henredon and Drexel. Damaged pieces are often expertly repaired to like-new conditions or left as is and priced accordingly. These prestige pieces are snatched up pretty fast, which is why people become *Roney* regulars, stopping in often to see what's new. From his previous store on East 14th Street in Oakland he has moved into an old National Guard Armory. At last you have a better chance to navigate around the stacks of furnishings. I've often been amused to see a stack of tires next to a fancy dining room hutch—but that's why *Roney's* is such fun. Upstairs you'll have four rooms of chairs—dining room, rockers, kitchen, maple, formal, etc.—to choose from. It's really impossible to list the different kinds of merchandise sold here, but it's worth a visit. Delivery is extra and you can save even more than the 30-60% off by carting it home yourself.

## SEARS FURNITURE OUTLET
1936 West Ave. 140th St., San Leandro 94577. Phone: 357-6622. Hours: T-Sat 9am-4:30pm. Purchases: Cash, Check, Store Charge. Parking: Lot.

Other Store: 3101 Kifer Rd., Santa Clara.

*Sears'* warehouse in San Leandro has a showroom which has (slightly) freight-damaged and returned furniture for sale at reduced prices. The customer returns have been reconditioned, and all bedding has been sterilized. There is usually a selection of more than 50 large appliances and televisions (your best buys here), and a smaller group of furniture, upholstered pieces, and mattresses. There are also accessory items, such as lamps, tables, and so forth. The Sears warranty applies to all appliances purchased. You must pay for delivery—so, if you can, bring a truck.

## ELSIE SMITH, INC.
945 Battery St., San Francisco 94111. Phone: 391-0717. Hours: W-Sun 11am-5pm. Purchases: BA, MC, VISA. Parking: Pay lot.

Located in the decorating center of San Francisco, this furniture warehouse store, with its plain, poorly lighted interior, has some great bargains on name-brand fine furniture. You can save as much as 30% retail on current domestic furniture. On closeouts or discontinued pieces from the same major manufacturers you can save as much as 40%. Delivery is extra, as are the freight charges on special orders.

Of special interest is the big selection of European reproductions of antique museum pieces. Connoiseurs of this sort of thing owe it to themselves to check for bargains.

## TRADEWAY STORES WAREHOUSE
(See **Carpets and Rugs**)

# Baby Furniture

## BABY WONDERLAND
22557 Mission Blvd., Hayward 94591. Phone: 581-4900. Hours: M, Th, F 9:30am-9pm; T, W, Sat 9:30am-6pm, Sun 11-5pm. Purchases: BA, MC, VISA. Parking: Street.

*Baby Wonderland* has one of the most complete selections of discount-priced baby furniture and accessories in the Bay Area. They have a large selection of quality clothes for infants and toddlers; selected names include Carter's, Health-tex, Buster Brown, and Pemay. You can choose from a complete line of cribs, mattresses, strollers, high chairs, car seats, etc. manufactured by such companies as Simmons, Strolee, and Hedstrom. Most everything is on display, so you can examine the goods to your heart's content. Almost all of the items carry two prices—the regular retail price and *Baby Wonderland's* discount price (usually at least 20% less). They also have a small catalog you can send for (or pick up when you are there); it contains many—but by no means all—of the items included in their stock. You should also sign up on their mailing list, which announces their large sales (friends say that these are definitely worth a trek to Hayward). They offer layaway, which is unusual for a discount store.

## ELEGANT STORK
(See **Clothing—Children's**)

## LOU'S BABY FURNITURE
221 Willow Ave., Hayward 94541 (½ block off Meekland). Phone: 581-6082. Purchases: BA, MC, VISA. Hours: M-Th 9:30am-5:30pm, Fri 9:30am-9pm, Sat 9:30am-5pm.

This is a most unconventional store. Years ago when this family wanted to get started in business they didn't rent a store downtown; instead they cleared out their garage and put up a sign. Their garage is now a small warehouse located behind the family home. Low overhead, no frills, and no advertising accounts for the low, low prices. All the

major brands of fine-quality furniture are available—everything for babies' needs except clothing and toys. Simmons, Thayer, Lullaby, Strolee, Peterson, Childcraft, and Hedstrom are among the brands represented in cribs, playpens, high chairs, dressers, infant seats, etc. All those hard-to-find repair parts will keep your furniture going through several children. They also have good values on used furniture. They accept trade-ins and layaways and also rent furniture.

## STORK TOWN
6800 Bancroft Ave., Oakland 94605. Phone: 562-0220. Hours: M-Sat 10am-6pm. Purchases: BA, MC. Parking: Street, free lot.

Their ads claim that *Stork Town* is "one of the largest complete one-stop discount baby stores in California." Certainly everything you could possibly need for baby's first year is here; every inch of wall space is covered with baby equipment, furniture, and layette needs. A limited selection of clothing is available, in infant sizes only. They have all the major name brands in baby furniture and equipment, most priced below department store prices. They carry replacement parts for cribs, strollers, and playpens (including replacement pads). Special mailings announce their super bargains. With twenty years' experience in the business, the owners can tell you just about everything you need to know regarding your baby's needs. Their motto is "if we don't have it, your baby doesn't need it!" Layaway is available.

# Unfinished Furniture

### DECOR
910 El Monte (corner of El Camino Real), Mountain View. 94040. Phone: 969-2008. Hours: M-F 9:30am-9pm, Sat 9:30am-5:30pm, Sun 12am-5pm. Purchases: BA, MC, FN. Parking: Lot.

Other Stores: San Jose, Santa Clara.

*Decor* has a tremendous selection of new unfinished furniture waiting for some loving hands to apply the finishing touches. Unfinished furniture stores are very competitive as far as prices go, but I think *Decor* has an edge because they are high-volume dealers and can get by with a smaller mark-up. Their newspaper ads in Peninsula and San Jose areas always feature some intriguing bargains.

The assortment of furniture is unbelieveable; you could furnish an entire house. I especially like the selection of cubes and modules, great for storage walls or displays. Maple, birch, oak, hemlock, ramin, mahogany, redwood, poplar, beech, pine, and even pressed board are there for you to choose from. Of course, harder woods do cost more, but there is a wide range of quality and price in their selection. All the finishing materials are here too—oil, stain, antiquing kits, etc. For the novice there's expert advice (no charge for this). There is a small delivery charge. Be smart and bring your van!

### NEW ERA UNFINISHED FURNITURE
4920 Telegraph Ave., Oakland. Phone: 653-3003. Hours: M, Th 9:30am-9pm; T,W,Sat 9:30am-5:30pm; Sun 11am-5pm. Purchases: BA, MC, VISA. Parking: Street.

*New Era* is one of the best stores in the East Bay for unfinished furniture. Not only is their selection unusual, but their prices are very good. I particularly liked the particle board cubes that are great for making storage walls in bedrooms or family rooms. New Era seems to be a "human" place where if there is anything you don't like about what you've bought, they'll fix it or take it back—pleasantly. They also deliver free on purchases over $20 in the East Bay.

# Warehouse Sales

*Capwell's, The Emporium, Macy's, Liberty House* and *W. J. Sloane's* all have major warehouse sales 2-3 times a year. The reason is obvious. Space is a problem in their warehouses just as it is in your closet at home. These sales are well advertised in all major Bay Area newspapers, usually accompanied with maps to lead you directly to these sites, far removed from the retail stores, most often located in some obscure industrial area. At these sales the major emphasis is on clearing out the hard lines of merchandise, i.e. furniture, appliances, and boxsprings, etc. However, accessories, remnant rugs, linens, and housewares are usually sold, too.

If you want first crack at the sale merchandise, you'd better bounce out of bed early on those week-end mornings because there are so many one-of-a-kind items, priced so low, that you can't afford to dally at home. All these sales are final. Usually delivery is extra, so if you want to save even more, borrow a pick-up from a friend and forget the delivery charge.

# Catalog Discounters

When it comes to buying new furniture for your home or office, the catalog discounters offer the best alternative to high retail prices. The businesses I have listed are all similar in that they take a lower mark-up, eliminate costly services, and usually don't advertise. Since their businesses are maintained on referrals and reputation alone, it is significant that they can be so successful without advertising. (You wouldn't send a friend to a place you'd been dissatisfied with.) Some of these places have no furnishings at all on their showroom floors; some have quite a lot. Most of their sales are from manufacturers' catalogs. Buying furniture this way will usually enable you to save from 20-40%. You'll pay for freight and delivery one way or another, whether they quote just one price or a break-down on the costs. Most do not have credit plans other than Mastercharge or BankAmericard.

**BARNAL FURNITURE CO.**
528 Larkin Street, San Francisco 94102. Phone: 771-0700. Hours: M-F 10am-5pm, Sat 10am-2pm. Purchases: BA, MC. Parking: Street.

This small furniture store is easily bypassed in the area around the Federal Building. They contend that there are 30% discounts on bedroom, dining room, living room, draperies, lamps etc; 25% savings on mattresses, Hide-a-Way Beds. Carpets are *their* cost plus $1.00 a yard. Appliances, TV's, stereos, etc., are cost plus 8%. Most merchandise is special ordered because their showroom is very limited in selection.

**DARIO'S FURNITURE & INTERIORS**
4727 Mission Street, San Francisco 94112. Phone: 333-1967. Hours: M-F 9am-5:30pm, Sat 9am-5pm. Purchases: BA, MC. Parking: Street.

A very accommodating gentleman owns this store. He tries to pass on the best discounts he has access to which ranges from 20-30% off on furniture. That includes all services, and 10% above "his cost" on appliances. A deposit is required with your order, balance on delivery.

## DOMICILE (formerly INNERHOUSE)

911 Sir Francis Drake Blvd., Kentfield 94904. Phone: 454-7881. Hours: T-Sat 10am-4:30pm. Purchases: BA, MC, VISA. Parking: Street.

Furniture, wallpaper, carpeting, vinyl and hardwood flooring, drapery and upholstery fabrics, custom bedspreads, accessories, window shades and blinds, are sold for 20-40% discounts at *Domicile.* The racks of samples and shelves of catalogs can be unnerving at first glance. The furniture selection is small but choice. Most customers special order with a 50% deposit, balance due on delivery. Delivery and freight are extra. I've noticed that they are very gracious about lending samples and they're equally helpful in assisting with selections. *Domicile* will be moving to larger quarters in Marin County in the fall of 1978.

## DUNNIGAN FURNITURE CO.

943 Columbus Ave., San Francisco 94133. Phone: 671-7990. Hours: M-F 9am-4:30pm, Sat and eves by appointment. Purchases: BA, VISA. Parking: Street.

The name is slightly misleading, since there is no furniture on display, only a large selection of catalogs of name-brand furniture, appliances, TV's, carpets, and draperies. You will save 25-30% on most orders, including freight and delivery charges. Since every item is a special order, there are no returns or exchanges. Bob Dunnigan, a businessman of long experience, gives personal, reliable service and will stand behind his merchandise. Business is on a cash basis, although BankAmericard is accepted on orders over $150. Long-term credit can be arranged through a nearby bank. A deposit is required with your order.

## EASTERN FURNITURE CO. OF CALIF. INC.

1231 Comstock Street, Santa Clara 95050. Phone: 248-3772. Hours: M,T,Th 9:30am-9pm. W,F,Sat 9:30am-5:30pm. Purchases: MC, BA. Parking: Lot.

Upon entering this store which is right off the Central Expressway you'll be greeted by a receptionist. She will provide you with a salesman who'll familiarize you with the showroom. There is a good selection of home furnishings including sofas, chairs, bedroom, formal dining, tables, mattresses, and even grandfather clocks. (No carpets or draperies sold here.) All are in the moderately priced lines. Don't be taken back by the price tags, which may not reflect the bargain prices you expect; you'll pay about 30% less. The styles are mostly traditional and you can choose from the floor selection or from their catalogs. This isn't the place to shop for those sleek contemporary styles. They ask you to be discreet about their prices. It's unfortunate that stores often have their lines jeopardized by the unthinking customer who quotes their prices to other retail stores. Let's not ruin a good thing!

I've been told that to shop here you need a membership card or referral. Check with them to see if your company is on their list, or call them to inquire about your shopping privileges.

## HOMEWORKS
370—Suite C, Park Blvd., Moraga 94556 (Rheem Shopping Center). Phone: 376-7750. Hours: Tues-Sat 10am-4:30pm. Purchases: BA, MC, VISA. Parking: Street.

This newly opened store in Moraga provides convenient shopping for Contra Costa shoppers. The store is small, more like a decorator's studio, but the resources for home furnishings are extensive. You can order carpeting, vinyl and hardwood flooring, drapery and upholstery fabrics, wallpapers, furniture and accessories from their samples and catalogs. Savings range from 20-40% off retail prices, depending on the price they can get. Delivery and freight are extra. They request a 50% deposit with the order and the remainder on delivery. The store is located at the back of the building next to a children's shop.

## HOUSE OF KARLSON
351 9th St., San Francisco 94103. Phone: 863-3640. Hours: M-Sat 9:30am-6pm. Purchases: BA, credit terms. Parking: Free at 445 9th St.

This store offers good savings on your home furnishing needs—sofas, chairs, bedroom and dining room furniture, TVs, and accessory items. They carry a large inventory of special purchases on rolls of carpet that were overstocked by leading manufacturers. Savings are impressive. Because they are located in a low-rent district, they are able to pass on substantial savings to their customers. "Preferred customers" are extended 25-30% off on their purchases. (I'm not really sure how they determine whether you will be extended preferred customer privileges,

though I was told that members of many business firms or large companies qualify. Be sure to inquire to see if you do, too.)

*The House of Karlson* is a full service store. Most brands in the medium to upper quality price range are carried or can be special ordered for you. I really enjoy their special newsletter, "The House of Karlson Courier," sent to their mailing list customers. It spotlights special purchases from major manufacturers, news and trends from the furniture industry, and tips on care and maintenance of your furnishings.

## HOUSE OF VALUES
2565 So. El Camino Real, San Mateo. Phone: 349-3414. Hours: M,Th,Sat 9:30am-5:30pm, M&F 9:30am-9pm. Purchases: BA, MC. Parking: Street.

It seems like *House of Values* has swallowed up several stores on this block. Just when I think I've seen everything I'm directed out the door and down the street to their next showroom. Many people reported on their outstanding selection and savings offered. I have to agree after comparison shopping their merchandise. Although they sell no carpeting or draperies, their in-store selection of fine qualiity dining room, bedroom, and living room furniture is quite extensive. You can save 30% and also have immediate delivery of your preference. They will also custom order furniture if they don't have the pieces you want.

## HOUSE OF LOUIE
(See **Appliances**)

## LAWRENCE CONTRACT FURNISHERS
(See **Carpets and Floorcoverings**)

## MASTER MART
2515 El Camino Real, San Mateo. Phone: 345-5271 or 341-3246. Hours: M-F 9-6pm, M&Th Eve till 9, Sat 9-5:30pm. Parking: Street. Purchases: BA, MC.

"Their" cost plus 10% is the inducement for many customers who've done business with this small store. They quote one price which includes all services, freight and delivery. Basically a custom catalog operation, I'd suggest that you shop around first because they have only a few pieces of furniture to show. They also sell appliances and carpets.

## MERIT FURNITURE
1899 Junipero Serra Blvd., Daly City 94014. Phone: 755-4311. Hours: M-F 9:30am-6pm, Sat 9:30am-5:30pm. Purchase: BA, check. Parking: Lot.

The friendly helpfulness of the salespeople is as impressive as the savings you will find at this catalog store. The showroom is small, but the number of items available through the catalogs is almost infinite. You'll save up to 30% on any item you choose; appliances are sold for cost plus 10%.

## MILLBRAE FURNITURE COMPANY
1781 El Camino Real, Millbrae. Phone: 589-6455. Hours: M,T,Th 10am-6pm, W.F 10am-9pm, Sat 10am-5pm. Purchases: BA, MC. Parking: Street.

Three floors of furniture, appliances, carpets, draperies, TVs, and stereo equipment make this a one stop resource for consumers. The furniture lines, top brand appliances are geared to the affluent peninsula shopper.

In their back room there are cabinets full of manufacturers catalogs that provide additional resources for their customers. On most items the savings run about 30% off prevailing retail prices. Like most discounters they don't advertise but do a steady business based on referrals.

## DAVID MORRIS CO.
1376 Sutter St., San Francisco 94109. Phone: 771-1376, 771-1377, 771-1378. Hours: M-Sat 9am-5:30pm. Purchases: BA, MC. Parking: Street.

This small company is little more than "a hole in the wall," but it offers big savings on furniture, appliances and especially carpeting. Scotty Morris is a real whiz at locating some of those hard-to-find franchise lines and items. His hottest item this year is the new video cassette tape recorder for television at a nifty price. You'll save 30% on almost all purchases, including freight and delivery. Everyone here is congenial. For those making large purchases, decorator assistance is available. A deposit is requested at the time the order is placed with the balance on delivery.

## NORIEGA FURNITURE

1455 Taraval (at 25th), San Francisco 94116. Phone: 564-4110. Hours: M,T,W,F 10am-5:30pm; Th 1am-9pm; Sat 10am-5pm. Purchases: BA, VISA. Parking: Street.

*Noriega Furniture* is highly appealing for two things in particular: their beautiful showroom and their personable decorator consultants. Their specialty is expensive, high-quality furniture; you can order from their manufacturers' catalogs everything you could conceivably need to decorate your home—furniture, carpets, drapes, wallpaper, and beautiful accessories—at savings of at least 20% and as much as 30%. Appliances are available at a cost plus 10% basis. They ask that you stop by the showroom to get an idea of what you want, though their decorators will go to most Bay Area communities with samples. You deposit 25-30% of the total when you order, and pay the rest on delivery (delivery is included in the price). All sales are final—no returns. They can arrange financing for you too.

## PARK FURNISHINGS

368 California St., Palo Alto 94306. Phone: 321-6480. Hours: M-F 9am-5pm, Sat 9:30am-4:30pm. Purchases: BA, MC. Parking: Street, lot.

*Park's* is a very gracious store in downtown Palo Alto. They will order exactly what you want and deliver it to you, ready to use for "their cost" plus 12%. My cost comparisons revealed that you save about 20%. Although their savings are not as great as other stores I've listed, the people there are very accommodating in assisting you with selections of carpets, bedding, furniture, and drapery needs.

## PIONEER HOME SUPPLY

667 Mission St. (4th floor), San Francisco 94105. Phone: 543-1234, 781-2374. Hours: M-F 9:30am-5:30pm, Sat 10:30am-2pm. Purchases: Cash, check. Parking: Street or pay lot.

Informality is the order of the day—there are always two phone calls on hold and at least three people waiting to place their order—but no one seems to mind because the savings are worth waiting for.

The owners (they must have a last name but they're Sam and Lucille to everyone) have been in business for over 20 years on the strength of their reputation and referrals that pass from one satisfied customer to another. They have never advertised, and you'd have to be psychic to discover them on your own.

You can buy almost anything in home furnishings from their floor samples or catalog resources: sofas, chairs, carpeting, also mattresses, appliances (only top-quality lines are carried in freezers, washers, and garbage disposals, etc.), microwave ovens, TV's, vacuum cleaners, and there's always a pile of electric blankets and mattress pads for sale.

The price they quote includes freight and delivery, and reflects savings from 20-40% below retail depending on what is purchased. (Savings on appliances are less than those on furniture and carpeting). You can order most merchandise with a deposit and the balance due on arrival if you're an established customer.

## PLAZA FURNITURE & APPLIANCE CO.
647 El Camino Real, South San Francisco 94080. Phones: 583-7050, 761-0866. Hours: M,T,Th,S 9am-6pm; W,F 9am-9pm. Purchases: BA. Parking: Street, lot.

You know after visiting this store that the entire staff has been in the business for a long, long time. Their experience shows as you discuss the merits of one piece of furniture over another, and which is the best value for the money you have to spend. I was particularly impressed with the selection of bedroom furniture for adults and children, although other types of furnishings are also well represented. The selection on display represents many moderate and higher-priced manufacturers. On the price comparisons I made, I would guestimate you'll save 25% on almost all of your purchases except appliances. Here's what you can buy: sofas, chairs, tables, appliances, TV's, stereos, lamps, carpeting, and draperies. On many furnishings and appliances you get quick delivery if they have your choice on hand in their warehouse nearby. Of course, other selections ordered from their catalogs will take longer.

## LEWIS SAMUELS
3320 18th Street (Bet. Mission & S. Van Ness). San Francisco, 94110. Phone: 861-4335 or 861-7765. Hours: M-Th 8:30am-6pm, F 8:30am-8:30pm, Sat 9am-4:30pm. Purchase: Cash, check. Parking: Street.

Get this address firmly fixed in your mind when you get ready to shop because you'll never believe you're at the right place. Lewis Samuels' showroom looks like an old apartment building on the outside; but the showroom displays represent many fine manufacturers of better furniture. You'll get sound advice, good service and best of all, no high pressure.

If the showroom doesn't display just what you're looking for, you can select your merchandise from their manufacturers catalogs. This is a complete home furnishings catalog store with catalogs and samples for appliances, drapes, carpets, bedspreads, woven woods, Levolurs, wallpapers and kitchen cabinets. They do expect a deposit with the order and the balance on delivery. You'll save a solid 30% on most items. Appliances are priced on a cost +10% basis.

## WESTERN CONTRACT FURNISHERS
4400 Broadway, Oakland 94611. Phone: 652-3400. Hours: M-F 9am-5:30pm, Sat 10am-3pm. Purchases: BA, MC. Parking: Private lot.

Other Stores: Carmel, Sacramento, San Francisco, San Jose.

*WCF* showrooms are simply beautiful. The furnishings displayed are the best and will appeal to people with discriminating taste and those who appreciate the best quality in home furnishings. However, if your budget is modest (starting out in your first home) you can still avail yourself of their facilities and good service.

Here is just a partial list of the types of merchandise you can order from approximately 2,500 catalogs they keep in their files: patio furniture; living, dining, bedroom, breakfast furnishings; mattresses; carpets and Oriental rugs; wallpapers; bedspreads; accessories; antique reproductions;

upholstery and drapery fabrics. The list is endless. Regardless of the style—contemporary, traditional, Early American,—their catalogs will provide the source and even after freight and delivery charges you'll still save approximately 30%. You have to pay in full when you place your order. You can use their bank financing plan, BA or MC. Of course, these options will cost you a little more.

To enable their salesmen to give you the best service, call in advance for an appointment, especially on Saturdays. There's no pressure here—something I like very much. Be sure to get on their mailing list for their semi-annual sales!

## HARRY YOUNG & CO
532 Columbus Ave., San Francisco 94133. Phone: 781-7010. Hours: M-Sat 10am-6pm, Tues 10am-9pm. Purchases: BA, MC. Parking: Street.

For years, Harry Young has been doing business with many members of Bay Area credit unions, but all customers are welcome. The atmosphere is relaxed, and like most discounters this store always seems to have more furniture than space to display it in. On most major brands of moderately priced furniture, you can save 25-30%. You can refer to one of their many catalogs for your purchases if the brand is not displayed in the store. Appliances are sold for cost plus 10% and on draperies and bedspreads you can save approximately 30%. Check here for TV's, stereos, vacuum cleaners, and carpeting. A deposit must be placed with your order and the balance on delivery. If you're on their mailing list you'll keep up with their biannual sales. Plan on waiting 8-12 weeks for items made in the East and Midwest.

# Office Furniture

(Also see **Furniture and Accessories—Catalog Discounters**)

## ARVEY PAPER CO.
(See **Paper Goods, Stationery**)

## THE DESK DEPOT
310 W. Evelyn, Mountain View 94041. Phone: 969-3100. Hours: M-S 9am-6pm. Purchases: BA, MC, VISA. Parking: Lot.

This place specializes in used office equipment. The selection is always changing depending on their sources. On the day I visited, there was a large selection of metal desks (what I call California State modern) than an earthquake wouldn't dent. Prices were around $100, very reasonable for something almost indestructible, if somewhat plain in appearance. You can also buy chairs, coat trees, tab card files, chalk boards, school desks, wastebaskets, etc. They have some new office furniture at 20-40% off list prices.

## OFFICE FURNITURE WAREHOUSE
935 Mariposa, San Francisco. Phone: 626-9453. Hours: M-F 8am-4:30pm. Parking: Street.

Beware!! Those railroad tracks that run right in front of the door of this warehouse accommodate trains that thunder by every half hour or so. I was so glad the manager asked me to move my car further away from the tracks—I never dreamed they were still in use as I parked my car just on the edge of them.

There is quite an assortment of office furniture in this drab, dark, unadorned warehouse. Some is ultrafancy modern, some obviously used. There are many desks, chairs, files, chair seats, hat and coat stands, etc. Occasionally James Hill must take returns on new merchandise that proves to be the wrong color or style for the client's needs. These rejects are sent back to the warehouse along with trade-ins from their contract jobs. You can save 30-50% on the selection here. Delivery is extra.

## REPO DEPO

1669 Bayshore Blvd., Burlingame 94010. Phone: 692-5000. Hours: M-F 9am-6pm, Th 9am-9pm, Sat 9am-6pm, Sun 12am-5pm. Purchases: BA, MC. Parking: Free lot.

Other Store: San Jose.

*Repo Depo* specializes in repossessed office equipment of all kinds. They have bits and pieces of almost everything in stationery supplies, too. The many prizes in office equipment range from electronic calculators to safes, from typewriters in excellent condition to expansive walnut desks with matching chairs. The back room contains many slightly damaged pieces of furniture at 30-40% less than regular retail.

Much of their used merchandise is priced very well, although some items seemed a little high. Generally, however, you can be sure to save money here on most general office equipment and supplies. New office furnishings are priced at straight retail. *Repo Depo* is specializing in telephone answering systems with all the appropriate interconnected accessories. They also have repossessed accounting systems, bookkeeping machines, word processing systems and other exotic electronic devices.

## RUCKER FULLER SOUTH—USED OFFICE FURNITURE

601 Brannan St., San Francisco 94107. Phone: 495-6895. Hours: M-F 8:30-6pm, Sat 10am-3pm. Purchases: BA, MC. Parking: Lot.

This is the clearance warehouse for *Rucker Fuller,* a firm that deals in only the best brands of office furniture. Their biggest customers are large companies willing to pay the price for quality and durability. Samples and manufacturers' closeouts are sent to this warehouse from the main store. Here there is also a large selection of good-quality used furniture received as trade-ins. The savings on the samples and closeouts may range from 40% off retail to below cost. The used furniture is priced according to condition and original price; you can expect to save from 40-60% off the original cost. All the defects or signs of wear are carefully pointed out to you by the manager, Marty Gillespie, who has had years of experience in this business.

# General Merchandise

## Catalog Discounters

The catalog discounter can make shopping a super bargain finding time for you. Most of the catalog companies carry a representative sampling of merchandise and a few special items that you won't see in the others. Prices can vary, too; comparative shopping pays off in dollars if you take the time to check out all the catalogs before you buy. All catalog sales operations have the same basic policies: returns are accepted within a certain period of time; there are no layaways; every article is guaranteed as described in the catalog. Prices quoted in the catalog are subject to change, but are basically rock-bottom low. Some places require that you have their special shopping pass, claiming that they are wholesale only (sometimes the pass is available for the asking, or you may be able to get one where you work.)

### BEST PRODUCTS
550 W. Hamilton Ave., Campbell 95008. Phone: (408) 374-6630. Hours: M-F 10am-9pm, Sat 10am-6pm, Sun noon-5pm. Purchases: Cash, check. Parking: Lot.

Other Stores: Citrus Heights, Mountain View, Pleasant Hill, Sacramento, San Jose.

*Best Products* claims to be the biggest consumer catalog company in the country. They have 40 showrooms throughout the U.S. with 6 stores in the Bay Area and more coming. Their 450-page catalog is the largest in the Bay Area; the prices are as good as the rest and better on some items. Sales are limited to cash and checks (keeps over-

head down). All merchandise has the full manufacturer's warranty and all the best national brands are carried. 94% of the merchandise in the catalog is on display and available immediately at their stores. It pays to look for their Tru-special tags (limited time sales) and Clearance tags (discontinued catalog selections) when you're in the showroom.

A convenient service at Christmas is the 24-hour telephone order service. It's to your advantage to obtain a *Best Products* card for $1 to become a preferred customer and be eligible for special sale opportunities. This catalog is a very good source for jewelry, sterling silver (30-50% off traditional store prices), and toys.

### CONSUMERS DISTRIBUTING
731 Market St. (at O'Farrell), San Francisco 94103. Phone: 737-2555. Hours: M-Sat 9:30am-9:30pm, Sun noon-5pm. Purchases: BA, MC. Parking: Lot (at most locations).

Other Stores: Antioch, Campbell, Capitola, Colma, Fairfield, Fremont, Hayward, Mountain View, Oakland, Pleasant Hill, Salinas, San Bruno, San Francisco, San Jose, San Pablo, San Rafael, Sunnyvale, Vallejo.

You don't have to wait for a sale to get a break! For really great savings, stop at one of the 28 newly opened *Consumers Distributing* catalog showrooms, which carry a complete stock of almost 5,000 first-quality name-brand items, including brands like Samsonite, Eastman Kodak, Spalding, Revere, and General Electric. The firm prepares its own catalogs of its merchandise twice a year, and tries to hold the prices listed throughout the lives of the catalogs. After browsing in the catalog, the customer fills out an order blank and hands it to a clerk, then receives the merchandise on the spot.

*CD* will accept for exchange or refund merchandise returned in the condition in which you would like to buy it (that is, unused, complete, and in the original carton). In the event of any merchandise defect, the makers will honor their guarantees and warranties.

## JEFCO MERCHANDISE, INC.

214 California St. (2nd floor), San Francisco 94111. Phone: 397-1232. Hours: M-Sat 9am-5pm. Purchases: BA, MC. Parking: Pay lots.

This is a bustling showroom where you can buy just about anything but clothing, toys, or large furniture items. An illustrated catalog is available for you to use at home. The manufacturer's suggested retail price is listed alongside *Jefco's* discount price; savings are 20-50% off on most merchandise. Special sale catalogs during the year offer even greater savings on selected merchandise. *Jefco* specializes in jewelry (diamonds, watches, and conventional and custom jewelry items). They also carry name-brand sports equipment and small appliances.

## KESSLER

2680 Union Ave, San Jose 95124. Phone: 408-371-3011. Hours: M,T,W,Sat 9:30am-6pm, Th & F 9:30am-9pm, Sun 12am-5pm. Purchases: BA, MC. Parking: Private lot.

See listing for *Davids of S.F.* Both stores were formerly operated by *Dahnkens Inc.*

## LEWIS LEAVY CO.

976 Mission St., San Francisco 94103. Phone: 781-5925. Hours: M-F 9am-5pm, Sat 9am-1pm. Purchases: BA, MC, store charge. Parking: Street, pay lot.

I walked past this store at least five times before I realized there was something going on inside, so innocuous is the exterior. Before entering the showroom you must stop at the reception desk and verify your shopping privileges. *Lewis Leavy* is a wholesale showroom where almost any item may be purchased for gift giving or home use. Small appliances, gift items, sporting goods, camping equipment, some toys, photo and stereo equipment, jewelry, and baby furniture are included in the selection. For convenience, merchandise may be ordered from their coded catalog. Order forms are available upon request. At the showroom, you fill out an order form from the coded tags on the displayed merchandise or from their catalogs. Merchandise may not be returned without written authorization from the store. All merchandise accepted for return must be in good condition and in the original carton.

## UNITY BUYING SERVICE

3491 Mission Oaks Blvd., Camarillo 93010. Purchases: Check, money order. Hours: Mail order only.

To obtain this company's 450-page catalog you must first become a member of their buying service, which will cost you $6. Write to the address above for membership information. With the local catalog discounters so readily available, you may wonder if the *Unity* catalog is necessary. I couldn't resist the urge to find out. Their catalog is much like those of all the other discounters; however, I was intrigued by the many items it has that the others don't, like garage door openers, heaters, tractors, and a wider selection of tools, all at very good prices. Ordering from *Unity* is more complicated than from the other discounters, because there is more involved: freight, service charges, tax, and insurance. But on many comparisons I made with merchandise from local catalogs, I found there were worthwhile savings on many, many items that ranged from 7-12% less, including all the extras. One large purchase would justify the $6 membership fee. With so many members (600,000) they have a lot of buying muscle; hence the great prices.

# Discount Stores

(Also see **Part II: Damaged Freight Outlets**)

You don't always have to drive miles out of your way to go bargain hunting. Throughout the Bay Area discount stores like *Payless, K-Mart, Gemco, Long's Drugs, Pay & Save, The Treasury, Value Giant,* and *Maximart* do a respectable job at pricing their merchandise lower than the full service retail stores. If you're in the habit of comparison shopping, and you can recognize a genuine sale price, you can do very well just by taking notice of the ads from these discount stores. Then, snap up those loss leaders they use as a lure to get you into the store. If you can resist buying non-sale merchandise at these times, you truly come out ahead. Books (hardcover and paperback), records, stationery supplies, paper goods, food products, plants, and small appliances are some of the best buys at these nearby, convenient discount stores. Don't overlook them!

**AKRON**
3951 Stevens Creek Blvd., Santa Clara 95050. Phone: 246-2700. Hours: M-F 10am-9pm, Sat 10am-8pm, Sun 10am-7pm. Purchases: BA, MC. Parking: Free lot.

Other Stores: Daly City, Mountain View, San Francisco.

Almost everyone knows about *Akron,* but if you have

never shopped there, you have missed some of the best bargains around. There are four stores in the Bay Area that maintain an unusual selection of merchandise at consistently low prices.

*Akron* has a unique inventory system; much of the merchandise is in their permanent inventory, but a large part is changing constantly because of erratic supply. These items are usually featured in the newspaper ads and they sell fast! People come in droves when these special ad items are placed on the floor, and the special items are often sold out the same day. If you have missed the bargain you longed for, you can fill out a stamped self-addressed postcard and they'll notify you when the item is available again. Not many big stores bother with this kind of service, but *Akron* does!

Their regular stock includes clothes for the entire family, household goods, wine and liquor, gourmet foods, art supplies, patio furniture, toys, garden supplies, hardware, and so forth. Just a few of the unusual items to be found at *Akron* periodically are authentic farm-worn milk cans, parking meters, and real New England spinning spools.

## COST PLUS IMPORTERS
2552 Taylor St., San Francisco 94133. Phone: 673-8400. Hours: Daily 10am-6pm. Purchases: BA, MC. Parking: Good luck!

Other Stores: Hillsborough, Mountain View, Oakland, San Jose, Walnut Creek.

*Cost Plus* is the largest and probably the best-known importer in the Bay Area. Their largest store, near Fisherman's Wharf, has almost become a San Francisco landmark. All that, and it is still probably the best place in the entire Bay Area to save money on all kinds of imported goods! This main store is so large that it is now housed in three adjacent buildings. The main store (the one that started it all) contains a complete dish and glassware department, and sections for clothes, baskets, toys, cookware, and papergoods. Furniture, objects d'art, and a nursery are in the other buildings. Some people have practically furnished their whole home from *Cost Plus*. There are few amenities here. Sometimes it's so crowded and so difficult to find a parking place that it's exasperating. But the atmosphere and the bargains usually pay you back for the inconveniences.

# Liquidators

## CONSUMER'S DISTRIBUTING CLEARANCE CENTER
1828 Norfolk, San Mateo 94403.Phone: 345-8467. Hours: M-F 10am-9pm, Sat 10am-6pm, Sun 12noon-5pm. Purchases: BA, MC. Parking: private lot.

You can't be as big as *Consumers Distributing* and not have some "problem" merchandise. Damaged, defective, discontinued, overstocked and returned items all end up here at the clearance center next to regional headquarters. Their repair department rights the wrongs, and then the items are placed on display shelves to be sold. The savings here just boggle the mind, 25-35% off the catalog discount price! You can expect to find anything here that is featured in their catalog. The selection changes all the time. All sales are final.

**MONTGOMERY WARD DISTRIBUTION CENTER**
3000 Alvarado St., San Leandro 94577. Phone: 357-7800. Hours: M-F 9:30am-9pm, Sat 9:30am-6pm, Sun 11am-5pm. Purchases: Cash, check, store charge. Parking: Free lot.

Other Stores: Richmond, Oakland.

This huge clearance center is where all catalog returns and discontinued, freight-damaged, and overstocked merchandise is sent. You can find just about anything that might be sold in their catalog from ankle socks to tractors. There are racks and bins of clothing and shoes, furniture, linens, carpets, home-improvement items, garden tools and equipment, TV's, appliances, etc. There is a 30-day guarantee on appliances or home entertainment items that are labeled "as-is" or freight-damaged. There is a delivery charge on this merchandise. Credit terms can also be arranged. Savings at the clearance center range from 10-50%.

Ward's has another store in Richmond at 211 Cutting Blvd. (just furniture and appliances). Their newest clearance center is located at the old Montgomery Ward Store at 2825 East 14th St., Oakland. It covers the whole first floor of this huge building and features a larger fashion selection than the San Leandro store, with some retail store returns in furniture and appliances plus a complete paint department.

# Giftwares

(Also see **General Merchandise—Catalog Discounters; Dinnerware and Accessories; Jewelry and Diamonds**)

**COST PLUS IMPORTERS**
(See **General Merchandise—Discount Stores**)

**CRESALIA JEWELERS**
(See **Jewelry and Diamonds**)

**DANSK II**
(See **Dinnerware and Accessories**)

**FARBER BROS.**
(See **Jewelry and Diamonds**)

**GIFT EXCHANGE**
3526 Geary Blvd., San Francisco 94118. Phone: 752-1208. Hours: T-Sat 10am-5pm. Purchases: Cash, check, trading stamps. Parking: Street.

This is one of America's unique stores—here's how it works. Take your unwanted but new and undamaged gift to the *Gift Exchange,* where they will determine the gift's current value based on their files of about 150,000 gift and houseware items. You may then select other items of equal value from their store display for a service charge of 20%.

For example, if your gift is worth $10, you select $10 worth of other items, and they charge you a service charge of $2. You may select items of higher value for the same service charge plus the difference. You may also use your credit at a later date; they will issue a credit slip.

The store includes an inventory of housewares, accessories, appliances, toys, paintings, leather goods, chinaware, silverware, toiletries, baby items, linens, and other items. The service charge and sales tax must be paid in cash or by check; they accept trading stamps.

If you have no gifts to exchange you still have a reason to shop here, since you'll receive 20% discount on any item in the store.

## M. JESSUP CO.
(See **Part II—Damaged Freight Outlets**)

## LUCITE OUTLET
1800 Industrial Way, Redwood City. Phone: 368-4161. Hours: M-F 9am-3pm. Parking: Lot. Purchases: Cash, check.

Serious buyers are welcome and browsers discouraged, as it's not as easy to shop here as it is at a regular store. You enter an office and are directed to a small display room by a receptionist. The back room features seconds and discontinued pieces from their impressive line of lucite giftware, hostess and kitchen accessories. There are minor flaws in many pieces: scratches or air bubbles in the lucite. The merchandise is not priced. After making your selection you have to go to the front desk and wait while they check their price sheets. I've always saved 50% off retail. I've been particularly pleased with the trays and super size salad bowls I've purchases. Be as brief and decisive as possible doing business here. They really can't tolerate wishy-washy buyers who take excessive amounts of their time.

## SAMPLE ROOM AND CANDLE FACTORY
37 Duffy Pl., San Rafael 94901. Phone: 457-3610. Hours: Daily 10am-5pm. Purchases: BA, MC, VISA. Parking: Free lot.

Tucked away in the industrial section of San Rafael is this treasure trove of candles, giftwares, pottery, toys, pictures, plaques, stationery, and so forth. The combined fragrances of the candles overpowers your senses; it's difficult to leave without buying at least two or three candles, especially since most of them are half off their original price. Big candles are sometimes sold by the pound! For the do-it-yourselfer, there is a complete selection of candlemaking supplies at super low prices.

The suggested retail price is listed along with the wholesale price on giftwares and decorator items. Most of this merchandise is acquired by special purchases of both domestic goods and imports. There are also close-outs, and samples from gift shows. Many items are one-of-a-kind, so if you find something you like, scoop it up fast. The bargain corner (merchandise that is slightly damaged or irregular) often has prices significantly below wholesale. This is a perfect place to shop for wedding, shower, and housewarming gifts. A word of caution: if you shop with your children, you are responsible for any breakage. All sales are final; no returns or exchanges are permitted.

**THE SECOND LOOK**
510 Broadway, Seaside 93955. Phone: 408-899-4442. Hours: M-Sat 11am-5pm. Purchases: BA, MC.

Turn your next trip to the Monterey Peninsula area into a bargain hunting expedition by stopping in at this outlet for Couroc products. This line which is sold in better gift shops and department stores is unique for its hand inlaid designs which give each piece its own character. Couroc products include trays, glasses, cheese boards, bronze sculptures and stoneware. Even as seconds, the quality is good and the prices are ½ off first quality retail prices.

**STUDIO AND SECONDS STORE**
(See **Dinnerware and Accessories**)

# Handbags

**GRIFFCO HANDBAG CO.**
373 4th St. (Mezzanine), Oakland 94607. Phone: 444-3800. Hours: M-F 10am-5pm, Sat 10am-4:30pm. Purchases: Cash, check. Parking: Street.

For casual, genuine soft leather handbags, you'll never find a better buy than right here at the *Griffco Factory Store.* All the handbags are well made. Many are lined.

You'll have 15-20 styles to choose from in several different colors. Most all the handbags are factory overruns and sell for approximately half the retail price. Factory prices range from $8.00-$24.00. The 2nds are priced even lower. To utilize all the scrap leather accumulated in the sewing room downstairs they've filled a showcase with coin purses, wallets, credit card holders, portfolios, and many other little leather accessories at good bargain prices. Another aspect of their business involves platform shoes, made to fit, and infants sandals. This outlet is off Broadway in the vicinity of Jack London Square.

# Jewelry and Diamonds

(Also see **General Merchandise—all headings**)

**AZEVEDO JEWELERS & GEMOLOGISTS, INC.**
210 Post St. (3rd floor), San Francisco 94108. Phone: 781-0063. Hours: M-F 9am-5:30pm, Sat 10am-4pm, eves by appointment. Purchases: BA, MC. Parking: Pay lots.

For substantial savings and a beautiful selection of diamonds, name-brand watches, and rare stones (emeralds, sapphires, jade, topaz, cat's-eyes, pearls, and rubies), this is a place well worth seeking out. *Azevedo Jewelers* has been in the same third-floor location for more than 35 years. Their success is owed to low overhead, careful and selective buying, and referrals from satisfied customers. Services include custom-designed jewelry and watch repair. You will enjoy doing business with Mr. Azevedo, who treats each customer with personal consideration.

## CRESALIA JEWELERS
278 Post St. (next to Gump's), San Francisco 94108. Phone: 781-7373. Hours: M-F 10am-5:30pm, Sat 9am-5pm. Purchases: BA, MC, VISA. Parking: Union Square Garage.

This store has been located on the second floor at 278 Post Street since 1912. It is evident that this is a very fine jewelry store when you alight from the elevator and enter the immaculate, luxuriously carpeted showroom full of gleaming displays of silver and showcases of fine jewels. There are no toasters or waffle irons, just the finest in jewelry and watches. You will also find a nice selection of silverware and dinner accessories here. The showroom will surely have just what you want right there on display.

Savings obtained here are substantially below those at other fine jewelry stores. (Because jewelry pricing is very complicated and varies from firm to firm, no hard-and-fast percentage can be quoted.)

## FARBER BROS.
73 O'Farrell St., San Francisco 94102. Phone: 421-0560. Hours: M-F 9am-5pm, Sat by appt. Purchases: BA, MC, VISA. Parking: Pay lots.

This is a first-quality store, airy and pleasant, with gracious service. Selective buying, volume sales, and low overhead enable the firm to offer substantial savings on personal jewelry—rings, name-brand watches, and diamond and gold jewelry. They also do custom design and make appraisals. For wedding gifts and other occasions, an extensive selection of silver flatware and hollowware (all those famous brands) is on display.

This store is located on the second floor; to reach it by the most direct route, go through the freight entrance at the O'Farrell Street address and up one flight of stairs.

## NIEDERHOLZER JEWELERS
140 Geary Street (4th floor) San Francisco, 94108. Phone: 421-7871. Hours: M-F 9am-5:30pm. Purchases: Cash, check, and terms. Parking: Street, pay lots.

For many years this has been a resource where "people who know" go for better quality jewelry at lower prices. The showroom on the 4th floor is just a block off Union Square. There are substantial savings on prestige brand watches, sterling silver flatware, hollow ware, personal gold and silver accessories, jewelry, diamond rings and rings or precious stones. The salespeople here are interested in customer satisfaction which means attentive service and fine quality merchandise.

## ZWILLINGER & CO.
760 Market St. (at Grant Ave.), San Francisco 94102. Phone: 392-4086. Hours: M-F 9am-5:00pm, Sat 9:00am-3pm. Purchases: BA, MC. Parking: Downtown garages.

To find this jewelry company first look for the Phelan

Building on Market Street, then make your way up to the 8th floor to Suite 800. You'll feel like you're entering a bank vault as you pass through their security doors. You'll feel more comfortable if you wear your Sunday best while in the presence of such beautiful jewelry.

For those great occasions in life—engagements, anniversaries, and graduation—where the remembrance you desire should be very special, a fine piece of jewelry can be purchased here at a considerable savings. Their prices on 14-carat gold jewelry were very impressive as well as their prices for watches and diamond rings.

# Linens

(Also see **Furniture—Catalog Discounters**)

**APRON TREE AND LINEN STORE**
(See **Women's Clothing**)

**CAPWELL'S BUDGET STORE**
(See **Family Clothing**)

**EMPORIUM BASEMENT STORE**
835 Market St., San Francisco 94103. Phone: 982-1111. Hours: M,Th,F 9:30am-9pm; T,W,Sat 9am-6pm; Sun noon-5pm. Purchases: Layaway, store charge. Parking: Downtown pay lots.

The entire basement floor of the *Emporium's* downtown store is a bargain bonanza, whose special buys are ad-

vertised in the San Francisco "Progress" twice a week. There is a constant flow of new merchandise in all departments: irregulars, manufacturer's overruns, returned shipments, off-season clothing. The selection of clothing is huge.

For the creative decorator and seamstress there are many exciting fabrics purchased from the ready-to-wear market (therefore not usually available to the public)—mill ends, shirt lengths, and closeouts. Unless you're a real fussbudget you'll be delighted with the fantastic savings on linens with very small irregularities, last year's patterns, or mill overruns. Savings are often more than 50%, really worthwhile when you're buying king-size sheets.

There are many one-day-only sales and the Basement Anniversary Sale in July. Conveniently enough, the BART Powell Street Station adjoins the basement store. All regular store services are available.

**EMPORIUM FURNITURE CLEARANCE CENTER**
(See **Furniture and Accessories**)

**MACY'S FURNITURE CLEARANCE PLACE**
(See **Furniture and Accessories**)

**MONTGOMERY WARD**
(See **General Merchandise—Liquidators**)

**WHEREHOUSE FOR BEDSPREADS, INC.**
729 Francisco Blvd., San Rafael, 94901. Hours: M,T,Th, Sat 10am-6pm, W-F 10am-9pm, Sun 12pm-5pm. Purchases: BA, MC, VISA. Parking: Street.

I'm amazed that any store that offers such a huge selection of bed and bath linens can manage to keep it all looking as neat and well organized as they do in this store. Their ability to offer 25-35% discounts is due to the fact that they buy directly from the manufacturer instead of the factory representatives. Their selection includes many styles of spreads, comforters, canopy sets, monogramed towels, satin sheets, throw pillows, floor pillows etc. Just about everything in linens is sold except blankets. The prices of the bedspreads range from $25.00-$200.00. If you can't find anything in their vast selection you can custom order a spread or comforter from their manufacturers' sample books and get a respectable discount.

# Luggage

(Also see **General Merchandise—all headings**)

**AAA LUGGAGE REPAIR DEPOT**
585 Howard Street (Near 2nd), San Francisco, 94105. Phone: 781-5007. Purchases: BA, MC. Hours: M-F 9am-5pm, Sat 9am-12:30pm. Parking: Street, pay lot.

You'll wonder where you are when you walk in the door because all the luggage, attache cases, trunks, totes, portofolios and wallets are in the back room. *AAA* is the authorized repair station for most national brands of luggage. Their specialty is trunks made from vulcanized fiber over plywood that is very strong and sold at great prices.

The back room is a clearance center of sorts for samples and retail store rejects that have been repaired. Savings range from 20-40% off. You may not be able to buy six matching pieces of luggage from their shelves, but most of us just looking for one or two pieces at a time will have no problem. Their attache cases are geared for the executive who may require special features for total efficiency and utility.

**BELGIUM RUG CO.**
1122 Howard St., San Francisco 94103. Phone: 863-4026. Hours: M-F 8:30am-5:30pm. Purchases: BA, MC. Parking: Street.

*The Belgium Rug Co.* (a rather misleading name, since they don't sell rugs) is a direct import firm open to the public. Their small showroom is cluttered with good buys on art objects, jade carvings, table cloths, vases, beaded handbags, small appliances, and many brands of Japanese stereos, watches and TV's, all discount-priced. I have found this is a good place to shop for soft luggage. You can save 30-40% off on luggage sets of the same quality as those in department stores. There are vinyl, canvas, and linen sets. My favorite is their flight bag for $10, just right for those short business trips.

## HARBAND'S LUGGAGE

517 Mission Street, San Francisco 94105. Phone: 986-2751. Hours: M-F 9am-5pm. Purchases: MA, BC, VISA. Parking: Street, lot.

The extensive selection of portfolios and attache cases makes this a very good gift shopping resource for the executive man or woman. Fine quality leather is their specialty, although, vinyls and hard cases are also available. Lark, Skyway, Ventura, Atlantic, Samsonite, Bayley Bags, and Halliburton are some of their lines but there's many more. Best of all you receive a 20% discount on all their merchandise. I was particularly pleased with their selection of better wallets, passport cases and travel accessories. Please note: they are closed on Saturdays.

# Paper Goods, Stationery

(Also see **General Merchandise—Discount Stores, —liquidators**)

## ARVEY PAPER CO.

111 Potrero Ave., San Francisco 94103. Phone: 863-3664. Hours: M-F 8am-5pm, Sat 9am-2pm. Purchases: Cash, check. Parking: Street.

Other Stores: Oakland, San Jose.

*Arvey* is a large manufacturer of paper goods and office supplies; their factory has almost any type of office

equipment or stationery you could think of. The display room is neat and well organized, and the salespeople very helpful. Delivery is available for a small additional charge. Special weekly sale brochures announce super buys to mailing-list customers.

You will save a minimum of 15-50% on all stationery goods, though I noticed substantially greater savings on some items. On office equipment, such as file cabinets and desks, you can save 15-40%. Janitorial supplies, such as tissues, mops, and paper towels, sell for 10-20% off. Printing supplies are a large proportion of their business; you will certainly save here. Returns and exchanges are gladly made if the sales receipt is presented.

## PAPER FACTORY OUTLET STORE

2060 Commerce Ave., Concord. Phone: 676-1023. Hours: M-Sat 9am-5pm. Purchases: BA, MC. Parking: Street.

Other Stores: San Carlos

Although this paper manufacturer specializes in institutional and commercial paper products like restaurant napkins, placemats, bathmats, hot dog and hamburger wrappers, toilet paper and paper towels, you can also find their selection augmented with party, stationery and wedding supplies. Their own products offer savings of up to 40%. Others at a modest 10-15% savings. There are good quantities of everything. Throughout the year they sell gift wrap by the foot, (you cut and measure yourself) at 6, 7 & 8 cents a foot depending upon the width. Some of the special items I've found fun to use are the spaghetti and fish bibs priced at 10/70¢. They can add a lively touch to a simple dinner.

# Shoes

I have tried to include those shoe stores with the best quality shoes at the lowest prices. Since you will be saving 20-60% off retail prices, you should be prepared to forego some of the creature comforts of a regular shoe store. Many stores are self-service, and you may have to dig into a pile to find what you want. To try on your discoveries, you may have to perch on a hard wooden bench or even lean against a wall. Since the stock consists strictly of factory closeouts, samples, cancellations, and seconds, there is a limited selection of sizes, colors, and styles.

**BRANDED SHOES OF BOSTON**
542 Lakepark Dr., Oakland 94106. Phone: 451-1088. Hours: M-Sat 10am-6pm. Purchases: BA, MC. Parking: Street, free lot.

Whatever shoe style you prefer, you'll find it here. It's a unique shoe store; current styles are available, along with high thin heels, pointed toes, platforms, boots, etc. This is a one-man self-service operation. All shoes are first-quality name brands in hard-to-find styles and colors. There is a small selection of men's shoes. Savings range from 25-50% off retail price.

**BROWN BROS.**
1416 34th Ave., Oakland 94601. Hours: M-Sat 9am-6pm. Purchases: Cash, check. Parking: Street, free lot.

If you are over 6'2'', you may have to duck a little as you make your way into this unusual shoe store located in the basement of a residential house just off East 14th Street in Oakland. Brown Bros. has been at the same location for 40 years (though it seems incredible that a business could operate so successfully in such an unconventional location).

This small store carries a selection of basic (conservative) men's shoes for work, dress, or sports. Several name brands (including Stacey Adams) are available, as well as many styles under their own label. Sizes through 13 are available in B-EEE widths, most shoes are in the $13-$20.00 range (which represents 30% less than retail). Service is friendly and personal.

**KUSHIN'S WAREHOUSE STORE**
22443 Foothill Blvd., Hayward 94541. Phone: 537-2411. Hours: M-Sat 10am-6pm. Purchases: BA, MC. Parking: Pay lot.

One of Kushin's regular shoe stores has been converted into an outlet for all the shoes that didn't sell at their other stores. Most of the shoes I saw were up-to-date styles, and there was a large selection of sizes and styles for men, women, and children. Prices are coded with colored dots on the soles; charts on the wall show the price that goes with each color. Nothing costs more than $18. Everything they have is out on the racks; you choose for yourself and try on alone (there is a cashier but no salesman). No returns are permitted.

**MARSHALL'S**
(See **Family Clothing**)

**MONTGOMERY WARD**
(See **General Merchandise—Liquidators**)

**ON A SHOESTRING**
1615 Bridgeway, Sausalito, 94965. Phone: 332-1661. Hours: M-Sat 10am-6pm, Sun 12pm-5pm. Purchases: BA, MC. Parking: Street.

Other Stores: 360 W. Portal, S.F.

It's hard to find buys in the Bay Area on good quality in-fashion shoes. By keeping in close touch with L. A. shoe jobbers, and buying in-season closeouts and left-overs, the owner is providing Marin County shoppers with real bargain opportunities.

Although the store is small, it is clean and comfortable and the displays encourage browsing. There is a good selection of men's, women's, and children's shoes. Prices are about half retail plus $1.00. Naturally you won't find all shoes in a complete size or color range.

**ROCKRIDGE SHOE HOUSE**
5123 Broadway, Oakland 94611. Phone: 658-5347. Hours: M-Sat 9:30am-6pm. Purchases: BA, MC, VISA. Parking: Lot.

You won't get salon shoe service here, but you won't expect the "extras" when you consider the prices. Ladies' shoes are their specialty (no men's or children's). Sizes range from 4-12, widths AAAA-C. Some of my favorite brands were displayed on their racks: DeLiso Debs, Jack Rodgers, Town & Country, Amalfi, and La Patti were just a few. The styles cover the entire fashion scene: clunkers to dainty, sophisticated dressy heels. The buyers travel to the out-of-state manufacturers and buy their odd lots and make-up orders. They also carry some inexpensive imports. Most shoes are under $20. The really expensive ones are of course a little more; for example, a pair that would cost $45 regular retail was marked $27. You can save 30-60% on the same shoes you see downtown. New shoes arrive weekly, so stop in often. They also mark shoes down continually to keep the inventory moving.

## SHOE FAIR

2049 Junipero Serra Blvd., Daly City 94014. Phone: 755-0556. Hours: M-F 9am-9pm, Sat 9am-6pm, Sun 11am-5pm. Purchases: BA, MC, VISA. Parking: Free Lot.

Other Stores: Campbell, Cupertino, Pleasant Hill, San Jose, San Rafael, South San Francisco.

*Shoe Fair,* the "House of Famous Brands," is a large, complete family shoe store. They have a large selection of sizes in casual, sporty, and dressy shoes. The styles vary from very conservative to wild and wonderful; brands range from obscure imported labels to well-known names like Joyce, Sbicca, Jarman, Verde, Puma, and Converse. On occasion, higher-quality imported shoes are available. One of the better selections of cancellation shoes is available here.

## SHOE MART

1041 W. El Camino Real, Sunnyvale 94087. Phone: 736-9836. Hours: M-F 9am-9pm; Sat, Sun 9am-6pm. Purchases: BA, MC. Parking: Free lot.

Other Stores: Millbrae, San Carlos.

A complete shoe store for the entire family, this shoe mart offers nationally known and advertised brands of good-quality shoes for men, women, and children. Making large purchases of overstocks allows this store to sell shoes at considerably lower than retail prices. The styles are up-to-date and selection of both size and style is excellent. Outstanding values are standard on work boots for men, sandals for women, and play shoes for children.

## SHOE RACK (LIBERTY HOUSE)

1501 Broadway, Oakland 94612. Phone: 891-2186. Hours: M,Th,F 9:30am-9pm; T,W,Sat 9:30am-6pm. Purchases: Cash, check, store charge. Parking: Downtown lots.

This shoe clearance center for all the *Liberty House* department stores always looks a bit hectic. As the shoe season evolves from fall to winter to spring to summer, all unsold men's and women's shoes are pulled from the other stores and sent to the *Shoe Rack* in the Basement of the Oakland store. Here they're immediately marked down 50%. There are frequent additional advertised mark-downs like 2 for 1, 1¢ sales, $5 off, etc. Here's your chance to get last season's $45 shoes for $5-$10. All sales in this department are final. After buying your shoes you'll want to stop in the basement clothing clearance section, where you'll find some good values on passed over, leftover, and last season's clothing.

## SHOE WORLD

880 El Portal Center, San Pablo 94806. Phone: 236-8121. Hours: M-F 9:30am-9pm, Sat 9:30am-6pm, Sun 11am-5pm. Purchases: BA, MC, VISA.

Excellent values in shoes for the whole family. There are many fine quality name brands available in prices from $5-$10, which represents savings from 25-75%. The shoes are purchased from volume lots, short lots, make-up orders, and manufacturer's overstocks—complicated buying techniques that result in low, low prices. Hard-to-find sizes are available as well as a complete selection of styles to suit every taste. Some of the ladies' shoes are not necessarily the latest style, but if you've a mind of your own and wear what you like regardless of what Madison Avenue dictates, you can really find some fine-quality classic styles. Many shoes are sold under their private label but are actually from quality makers such as Red Cross and Cobbie. I was especially pleased to find some of those expensive name-brand children's shoes available here. This is also a clearance center for a well-known Bay Area quality shoe chain.

## STANDARD SHOE MART

300 El Camino Real, Millbrae 94030. Phone: 697-4014. Hours: M-F 10am-8:30pm, Sat 9:30am-6pm. Purchases: BA, MC. Parking: Free lot.

*Standard Shoe Mart* is a liquidator; they have shoes for the entire family at 30% and more off regular retail. Many styles, sizes, and brands are here in incredibly large numbers. The place is roomy and comfortable. There are salespeople ready to help you when you need it (but not before), which makes this one of the very nicest shoe discount stores to shop in.

# Sporting Goods

(Also see **General Merchandise—all headings**)

## BIG 5 SPORTING GOODS

314 Gellert Blvd., Daly City 94015. Phone: 994-3688. Hours: M-F 10am-9pm, Sat 9am-9pm, Sun 10am-8pm. Purchases: BA, MC. Parking: Free lot.

Other Stores: Corte Madera, Mountain View, San Jose, Terra Linda.

*Big 5* has made its good reputation by offering sporting goods at prices 20-40% below regular retail prices. Whatever your interest—fishing, golf, tennis, badminton, camping, hunting, or bowling—you'll find all your equipment here. The store buys in huge quantities and carries all the major brand names for each sport. All their ten Northern California stores are sparkling clean and well organized; their salespeople are sports enthusiasts, too, and can offer helpful advice in choosing appropriate equipment.

*Big 5's* merchandising policy of offering sales during the actual season of any sport means you don't have to wait. Sometimes they will have closeout merchandise at even greater savings. Look for the ads on Wednesdays, Thursdays, and Fridays in your local newspaper.

**MERCHANDISERS INC.**
(See **Men's Clothing**)

**THE NORTH FACE FACTORY OUTLET**
1234 5th St. (off Gilman), Berkeley 94710. Phone: 524-8432. Hours: M-Sat 10am-6pm. Purchases: BA, MC. Parking: Street.

All you Sierra Club types and fresh air fans take note: *The North Face* manufactures functional outdoor equipment. Their aim is to provide versatile gear for comfortable and efficient wilderness travel in all climates, conditions, and places.

Their factory outlet features four categories of bargain merchandise with savings of 20% on all their seconds. These include clothing (parkas, hoods, vests for men, women and children), backpacks, sleeping bags, accessories, and even tents. Occasionally they have Voyager or Lowa boots, although the sizes available are limited. All the seconds are functional and have only cosmetic flaws such as a run or snag in the fabric, off color or

patch. You can also save 40% on used ski touring equipment.

The manager, Brian Birmingham, has all the up-to-date information on local climbing and hiking conditions.

**R.E.I. CO-OP**
1338 San Pablo, Berkeley 94710. Phone: 527-4140. Hours: MTF 10:30am-6:30pm, W&Th 10:30am-9pm, Sat 9am-5pm. Purchases: BA, MC. Parking: Lot.

If you're involved in any activity or sport that requires special equipment or clothing, *R.E.I.* offers their customers and *Co-op* members good prices and a complete selection. For $2.00 you can join their *Co-op* which entitles you to a dividend at the end of the year based on your purchases. All the people I know in Scouting, backpacking, skiing, rafting, golfing, tennis, et al. check *R.E.I.* prices first. On my comparisons with other sports equipment company catalogs, *R.E.I.* came out ahead both in price and quality. In all equipment lines they offer several qualities and price ranges. It's up to you to determine what your investment should be depending upon your involvement in your sport and the use you hope to get out of your purchases.

**SECONDS BEST MOUNTAINEERING**
2042 4th St., San Rafael 94901. Phone: 457-5544. Hours: M-Sat 10am-5:30pm, Sun 12pm-5pm. Purchases: BA, MC. Parking: Lot.

This little hole in the wall is just crammed with goodies for the mountaineer. You can save 20% on name brands like Snowlion, Class 5, Campy and Wilderness Experience.

These seconds may have a stain, uneven stitching, or small snags, basically cosmetic flaws which do not impair the usefulness of the assortment of down bags, polarguard bags, parkas, packs, ponchos, tents, or rain gear. All sales are final. Watch for their ads in the "Classified Gazette."

## SIERRA DESIGNS
4th and Addison, Berkeley 94710. Phone: 843-2010. Hours: Th 4pm-8pm, F 12pm-6pm, Sun 10am-5pm. Purchases: Cash, check.

*Sierra Designs* makes mistakes too! You can find their seconds stashed away in a corner of their production warehouse. Everything is reduced 20-30%, such as down sleeping bags, jackets, tents, wool shirts, occasionally packs and other related backpacking, cross-country skiing, and mountaineering equipment. The hours are very limited and you can call their regular store for information on what's available in the outlet.

## SKI EXCHANGE
(See **Part II: Charity and Rummage Sales**)

## SKI SWAP
(See **Part II: Charity and Rummage Sales**)

## SPORTS EXCHANGE
2121 Staunton Ct. (off El Camino and Oxford), Palo Alto 94306. Phone: 321-9610. Hours: M-Sat 10am-6pm, Th 10 am-9pm.

A first-of-its-kind recycled, sporting equipment outlet

where people can buy, sell, trade, or repair **used** bicycles, skis, tennis rackets, golf clubs, balls, camping gear, etc. Customers bring in their used sports equipment and receive cash for it, or they may place it on consignment (they receive 60% of the selling price) or they may trade it in on other merchandise in the store. If goods are in need of repair, they are reconditioned by the *Sports Exchange* before being placed on display. Periodic team equipment exchanges, such as Soccer Shoe Swaps, backpacking and ski swaps, are also conducted.

So that you can test the merchandise there is a tennis rebound court, artificial turf golf putting area, bicycle "test driving" accommodation, tennis shoe resole facility and fully-equipped repair shop. This is a great place to outfit your children at budget prices!

# Stereo, Hi-Fi, Components

(Also see **General Merchandise**—all headings)

# General

## EMPORIUM FURNITURE CLEARANCE CENTER
(See **Furniture and Accessories**)

**HALTEK ELECTRONICS**
1062 Linda Vista Ave., Mountain View 94043. Phone: 969-0510. Hours: T-Sat 9am-5:30pm. Purchases: BA, MC.

Other Store: Santa Rosa.

*Haltek* carries all those esoteric electronic components, i.e. TV tubes, batteries, transistors at 40-50% off. To keep on top of the market involved in ecology and energy saving products, they're selling parts for solar panels, motors for wind power generators, etc.

**HOUSE OF LOUIE**
(See **Appliances**)

**MACY'S FURNITURE CLEARANCE PLACE**
(See **Furniture and Accessories**)

**PACIFIC STEREO**
2702 No. Main St., Walnut Creek 94596. Phone: 933-9900. Hours: M-F 9am-9pm, Sat 10am-6pm, Sun noon-6pm. Parking: Street. Purchases: BA, MC.

Other Stores: Concord, Hayward, Larkspur, Mountain View, Sacramento, San Francisco, San Jose, Santa Clara, San Mateo, San Rafael, Colma.

When it comes to purchasing stereo systems and equipment most people tend to overlook the obvious. *Pacific Stereo* splashes big ads throughout Bay Area newspapers with such frequency that many people assume that all their advertising will result in higher prices. Yet, because they are the biggest volume dealer in California (approx. 60 stores), it is possible for them to offer tremendous values on most of their merchandise. You can often wheel and deal and walk out with an entire system at 10% above cost. A lot depends on your assertiveness.

The mark-up on stereo equipment is about 25-30% above wholesale. There is a higher mark-up on their own store brands, a smaller mark-up on some of the finer quality, more expensive lines. The larger mark-ups are on loudspeakers, turntables, and accessories. You have the best chance for negotiating a special deal when you are buying a whole system. On their prominently advertised "loss leader" items (that sends competitors into a spin) prices are firm. Don't expect to dicker on these low prices.

For the novice, a few suggestions: never put yourself at the mercy of a hi-fi salesman. Determine your budget *first,* then check the rating in Consumer Reports and Consumer Guide. Use them as a general guide. *Pacific Stereo* offers a good warranty and very important, a reliable service department.

**QUEMENT**
1000 S. Bascom Ave., San Jose 95128. Phone: 998-5900. Hours: M-Sat 9am-6pm. Purchases: BA, MC, VISA. Parking: Free lot.

*Quement* is a complete stereo sound center located in a huge warehouse-like building, with 40,000 square feet of electronic parts, components, tubes, accessories, antennas, and ham gear. They have most well-known brand names, including Dual, Marantz, Sony, and

Garrard. The prices here are "wholesale to all"—all who make the trip to *Quement.* Since they have been in business since 1933 and do a tremendous volume (they even sell to other commercial and industrial outfits in the southern Peninsula area), they can offer low low prices to you stereo and ham operator bugs. They also have a complete service department to help you with any problems.

## RECYCLED STEREO

2797 Shattuck Ave., Berkeley 94705. Phone: 843-2831. Hours: M-F 10am-9pm, Sat 10am-6pm, Sun noon-6pm. Purchases: BA, MC. Parking: Free lot.

*Recycled Stereo* is an outgrowth of *Pacific Stereo's* trade-in policy on new equipment. It provides access to used high-fidelity equipment for those who couldn't otherwise afford it. There is a large and constantly changing selection of legitimate bargains in everything from compacts to some very exotic stuff. You can expect to save about 50% off the original retail price of this merchandise, a painless way to acquire some good-as-new stereo gear.

All parts and components are tested (and repaired, if necessary) by the service center before being offered for sale. Most equipment is covered by a 90-day warranty on parts and labor. Some gear will be sold "as is" at even lower prices for those who like to do their own recycling. Their bulletin board provides a space for you to post your stereo-recycling projects or to find out who needs your help. All sales are final.

## E. C. WENGER ELECTRONICS CO.

1450 Harrison St., Oakland 94612. Phone: 451-1020. Hours: M-Sat 9am-5:15pm. Purchases: BA, MC, store charge. Parking: Free lot, metered street.

Other Stores: Redwood City, San Leandro, Walnut Creek.

I'm a little out of my depth in a store specializing in electronic needs. The merchandise—all 50,000 varieties of tubes, meters, cables, plugs, transistors, antennas, batteries, and items so foreign to me I couldn't begin to describe them—is neatly arranged on rows and rows of pegboards and display shelves. The original wholesale electronic store in the Bay Area, this is the place where all my do-it-yourself friends head for real savings, expert advice, good service, replacement parts for TV's, stereos, and radios, and the knowledge that hard-to-find items can be special-ordered with great expediency. Of interest is the large selection of technical books, the assortment of speaker cloth (neatly displayed on wall-mounted rolls), and the demonstration room for home interior speaker sound systems.

Approximately 85% of the inventory is 20-40% off retail prices. Tubes are always a great bargain at 40 to 60% off (all sales final on these). Be sure to watch the local papers for special sales.

## WEST COAST AUDIO

1423 W. San Carlos Ave., San Jose 95126. Phone: 292-9545. Hours: M-F 9am-9pm, Sat 9am-6pm. Purchases: BA, MC. Parking: Street.

*West Coast Audio* is a supplier to many of the well-known larger retailers in the San Jose area. They have in stock over 30,000 items; the thing you need is probably one of them. You can save 50% by filling all your electronic parts needs here. If you're a beginner, go with someone who knows what parts of equipment you want; the busy clerks here are reluctant to offer help or advice to novices.

# Toys

(See **General Merchandise**—all headings)

## TOYS 'R' US

1082 Blossom Hill Rd., San Jose 95123. Phone: 266-2600. Hours: M-F 10am-9pm; Sat, Sun 10am-7pm. Purchases: Cash, check. Parking: Free lot.

Other Stores: Daly City, Hayward, Pleasant Hill, Sunnyvale.

These stores offer good prices on most items, and sometimes you can find a particular item at a lower price than you would find anywhere else. The children's books and party goods, for example, are usually the lowest in town. These stores are all huge warehouse-like buildings, each one with thousands of low-priced toys for every age group, making selection a frustrating experience. The stock is well organized into sections: games, preschool toys, infant furniture and supplies, bicycles, books, novelty items, dolls and stuffed animals, playground equipment, and paper party goods. At these discount prices, you do give up some of the traditional services. There is no gift wrapping and no layaway or will-call plans. Displays permit you to see and touch what you are interested in. The policy is ''no-questions-asked money refund'' if you furnish the receipt and the toy is in its original carton.

## TOY WAREHOUSE SALES

1256 Howard Street, San Francisco 94103. Phone: 863-8346 or 863-8665. Hours: M-Sat 9am-5pm. Purchases: Cash, check. Parking: Street.

This company imports several types of merchandise that they sell to retail stores throughout the country. Before Xmas 1977 they decided to allow the public to buy surplus inventory from their warehouse, at prices just slightly over wholesale.

Their most popular items, available in seemingly endless quantities, were stuffed animals (Beatrice Potter types; available individually or in different sets), wooden pull toddler toys, trains, and forts. They import a delightful line of infant accessories which consist of quilted gingham checked crib blankets, bibs, infant seat covers, pillow shams, etc. These can be purchased as complete sets or by the piece.

Before making a trip, I'd call to be sure they're open. Typical of warehouse operations, you have to locate the address and the doorway and proceed up a flight of stairs before you arrive at their showroom.

# Wallpaper

## DISCOUNT WALLPAPER
149 E. El Camino Real (at Grant Rd.), Mountain View 94040. Phone: 969-7466. Hours: M-F 10am-6pm, Sat 10am-5pm. Purchases: MC, BA. Parking: Lot.

When a wallpaper manufacturer deletes a pattern or line from its catalog, whatever is left becomes excess stock. Many distributors will not buy such noncurrent merchandise, but this enterprising store does and offers it to the public at very low prices, usually 50% off. Types range from budget paper rolls to vinyl and textured varieties. Some papers come in limited quantities and cannot be reordered, so measure carefully before you buy. You can also order from current wallpaper books but the savings are not as great—only a 10% discount unless there is a manufacturer's sponsored sale on at that time. Along with wallpapers there is always a good selection of fabrics at 30-40% savings, sometimes as low as $1.50/yard.

## LAWRENCE CONTRACT FURNISHERS
(See **Carpets and Flooring**)

## SEM PAINT COMPANY
Sem Lane & Shoreway Road, Belmont (Bayshore Fwy, next to Holiday Inn). Phone: 592-5752. Hours: M-F 8am-5pm, Sat 8am-4:30pm. Purchases: BA, MC. Parking: Lot.

*SEM* carries wallpaper from 10 major suppliers. Each book has a tag which tells you the percent of discount. Discounts on books range from 10-25%. Additional discounts are available during wallpaper manufacturers' sponsored sales.

Occasionally they sponsor free wall paper "How-to-hang" classes. *SEM* also sells paints at 30% discount, and paint sundries at 20% off. There is a 20% handling charge on all returns.

## WALL COVERINGS UNLIMITED
2680 El Camino Real, Santa Clara 95051. Phone: 408-247-4976. Hours: M-Sat 10am-6pm, Sun 12am-4pm. Purchases: MC, BA. Parking: Lot.

All wallpaper books are 10-20% off and further discounted when the manufacturers have an advertised sale. For the ready-to-get-started, the best feature is their in-store stock of approximately 300 current patterns and 250 discontinued patterns. They often have the hottest new patterns available in special manufacturers strike-offs (the colors are changed) at 30-40% off.

You can follow their frequent special sales in the San Jose "Mercury". It's possible to custom order your papers over the phone using a Bankamericard or Master Charge and then have the paper shipped directly to your home.

A small selection of discontinued fabrics for home decorating is usually piled on a table for 99¢/yard. Woven woods and Levolors are discounted 20-25%.

## WALLPAPERS TO GO

2940 Geary Blvd., San Francisco 94118. Phone: 668-2290. Hours: M-F 10am-9pm; Sat, Sun 10am-6pm. Purchases: BA, MC. Parking Lot.

Other Stores: Cupertino, Daly City, Larkspur, Pleasant Hill, Sacramento.

This is a wallpaper supermarket, unique because there are no wallpaper books. Next to each wallpaper sample stand there is a bin full of matching rolls. You simply mosey up one aisle and down another looking at their vertical fixed samples until you find the one you want. Load up with the number of rolls you need. They're real pros at helping you figure this out and best of all, before the mood escapes you, you can go home and get started immediately. They also sell you all the "fixings."

Most papers are priced in a range from $1.44-$11.00. Most name brand companies are represented. Many papers are bargain priced because they represent closeouts and discontinued patterns. They're often marked down 50-60%. Exchanges are possible within 30 days if the sales receipt is furnished. Also, refunds are possible on unused rolls. For the real beginner—step to the demonstration center at the back of the store and watch a brief movie on how-to-do-it or catch one of their demonstrations. You'll have no excuse for getting yourself caught between the paper and the wall!

## WESTERN CONTRACT FURNISHERS
See **Furniture and Accessories—Catalog Discounters**)

# Window Treatments

WOVEN WOODS, SHUTTERS, LOUVERS

You don't ever have to pay full retail prices on shutters, woven woods or louvers (Levolor, Riviera and Flexalum). Stores that sell this merchandise, large retailers like *J.C. Penney, Sears, Home Yardage, New York Fabrics,* and small specialty stores, have sales 2-3 times a year and offer a 20-25% savings. On the whole, most stores are reluctant to announce when their set sales occur. However, it doesn't hurt to ask if there's going to be a sale, even if they won't say. You don't have to do it aggressively. Use politeness, tact and skill. Watch the newspapers closely and be patient. If you really can't wait for a sale by a retailer, refer to the Furniture Section: Catalog Discounters. Many of these stores listed sell woven woods and louvers at a 20-25% discount all year round.

Part Two

# Sometimes Tearfully Abandoned, Almost All Previously Owned, Some New, Perhaps Damaged, But All in All, Useful and Usable Merchandise

# Auctions

Art and nostalgia combined have made the auction big business in California. Sometimes the bargains are fantastic . . . sometimes they're not.

Auctions must be announced in advance, and this is generally done in the Sunday edition of the metropolitan newspapers, under "Auctions." Most of the art and real estate auction firms have descriptive brochures of items to be sold, and offer previews prior to the sale.

Bidding at almost all auctions proceeds according to the mood and pocketbook of the crowd. Size up your competition: customs, police, and railroad auctions attract average citizens, while art and antique auctions appeal to the moneyed collectors.

Many auction houses require a buyer's registration prior to the sale; others have a loose "walk in and bid" arrangement. Purchases are usually by cash, or by certified or cashier's check.

There are many different types of auctions listed on the next few pages. Take your choice and have fun.

## Art and Furniture

Follow the classified ads of the following auction houses for antiques, furnishings, estate sales and art objects. There are many good auctions in the Bay Area, but I have found the following to have auctions more frequently and with a larger selection of goods than most.

**AARCO AUCTION STUDIO**
661 Golden Gate Ave., San Francisco 94102. Phone: 863-3850. Hours: Previews: Tues. 10am-4pm. Auctions occur on Wed. at 11am every 3-4 weeks. Mailing list by request. Parking: Street.

**ATHERTON AUCTION STUDIO**
2317 Broadway, Redwood City. Phone: 366-2944 or 326-0958. Hours: M & T Evenings at 7:30pm, usually held twice a month. Mailing list by request. Specializes in antiques and estates.

## HARVEY CLAR'S ESTATE GALLERY

4364 Piedmont Ave., Oakland 94611. Phone: 428-0100.Hours: Preview Sat & Sun 12noon-5pm, Auctions every 3 weeks M,T,W, evenings at 7:30pm (subject to change). Mailing list by request. Purchases: BA,MC. Parking: Private lot.

## KING AUCTION STUDIO

1825 Salvio St., Concord 94520. Phone: 689-1897. Hours: Preview T,W 9am-5:30pm, Auctions Wed. & Fri. at 7:30pm. Purchases: Cash, check. Parking: Lot.

## McCOY AUCTION CO.

22366 Fuller Ave., Hayward 94511. Phone: 785-2818. Hours: Antique auctions T-Th 7:30pm (subject to change). Purchases: BA,MC.

# Police

Local police departments hold auction sales to dispose of goods which were confiscated in police cases but not reclaimed by their original owners. The range of merchandise is limited only by the ingenuity of the burglar. Bicycles are the hot items at these sales, followed by radios, tape decks, televisions, small appliances, cameras, tools, and furniture. Sometimes there is no prior inspection of merchandise, so bid with care. It's all sold "as-is", strictly cash-and-carry. Bidding depends on the mood and pocketbook of the crowd, and since buyers are usually average citizens, bargain buying pevails. Auction dates must be publicized in local newspapers. Call your local department to find out when the next auction will be, mark it on your calendar. The sales usually begin about 9am and last until mid-afternoon.

San Francisco is the only police department that holds regular monthly auctions. Starting at 9am they are held at the Hall of Justice, 850 Bryant St., (basement), San Francisco. For dates and information call 553-0123.

# U.S. Government

## U.S. BUREAU OF CUSTOMS

630 Sansome St., Room 400, San Francisco. 94114. Phone: 556-4340. Purchases: Cash only. Parking: Street.

Several auctions are held each year by the *U.S. Department of Customs* to dispose of the thousands of items confiscated by San Francisco customs agents for various violations of the Tariff Act of 1930. Many unique articles from all over the world take this route to auction block. Items up for auction are liquor (which goes for about the same as regular retail, because bidding starts at the amount of federal tax on each item), clothing, cutlery, cameras, watches, lamps, pottery, gift items, jewelry, radios, tools, and some furniture. While some of the auction prices here are close to retail, many sell for 50% or less.

You can call the bureau and have your name put on the mailing list. They will mail you a small catalog that describes the articles for sale and tells you how to become a bidder.

## U.S. POSTAL SERVICE AUCTIONS

Civic Center (Polk & Grove), San Francisco 94102. Phone: 556-2500. Hours: About every 3 months. Purchases: Cash only. Parking: Street.

San Francisco is the dead letter and package center for California; all lost and unclaimed mail ends up here. It is auctioned periodically depending on how much mail has accumulated; usually, however, an auction is held about every 3 to 6 months. All items are just as they were received at the post office. Both single items and lots are sold; almost anything a person could conceivably mail might be included. The dead letter center sends bulletins to all post offices designating times of auctions. It's best to call, though, and have your name put on the mailing list.

# Charity and Rummage Sales

## OAKLAND MUSEUM WHITE ELEPHANT SALE

Oakland (address to be announced). Phone: 893-4257 for information. Hours: To be announced. Purchases: Cash, check.

This sale, conducted by the Oakland Museum Women's Board, is one of the most successful fund-raising efforts in the Bay Area each year. In 1978 the sale earned more than $200,000! It is usually held in a different downtown

Oakland location each February (last year in an empty department store scheduled for demolition).

Every possible type of merchandise is available for sale, including large quantities of new, first-quality goods donated by local merchants. One store donated 5,000 pairs of new shoes for the sale! Clothing is popular and accounts for a substantial portion of the sale; it is always arranged neatly in department-store style on racks according to size and quality. There is an elegant designer section, a better-dress section, a nice selection of furs—and budget dresses as low as $1. There are linens, toys, housewares, books, records, appliances, and great buys in furniture.

Last year I purchased a sturdy though somewhat worn desk for $11. After I antiqued it and fitted it with new hardware, I could hardly recognize my ugly duckling.

The sale is announced in newspapers and on radio and television.

## SKI EXCHANGE

Lafayette School Playground, 950 Moraga Rd., Lafayette 94549. Hours: Annually, usually a Saturday in October. Purchases: Cash, check. Parking: Street.

A much-waited-for event each fall in the East Bay is the highly successful *Ski Exchange* conducted by the enterprising ladies of the Maytens Branch of Children's Hospital Medical Center. It is usually held in Lafayette (at the Lafayette School Playground the last few years). The 1973 sale took place on October 13, from 9am until 4pm.

*The Ski Exchange* is a clearinghouse for individuals and retail stores wishing to dispose of obsolete clothing and equipment in the hope of recouping some of their initial investment. Individuals wishing to sell their goods are charged a small fee for the opportunity. For instance, to sell a pair of skis you may be charged $2; you may then charge whatever you want for the skis. People I knew were there the first thing in the morning to have the first crack at the children's clothing and equipment. The bargains run from the ridiculous to the sublime. You're sure to save 24-75% on new, slightly soiled, and used gear. Everyone benefits from this event!

The sale is usually publicized in the Oakland "Tribune" and the green Sports section of the San Francisco "Chronicle."

### SKI SWAP

Brooks Hall, Hyde & Fulton, San Francisco, Phone: For information call 558-5065. Hours: Annually, usually in the fall. Purchases: Cash, check. Parking: Pay lot.

This annual ski swap, conducted by the Alpineer Ski Club with assistance from the Peninsula and Viking ski clubs, is a must for all skiing enthusiasts. In addition to the bargain prices, there are musicians, ski movies, dancers, exhibits, and a ski auction. The U.S. Ski Team benefits from the proceeds from the auction; items sold are donated by local merchants.

People interested in selling used ski equipment register their gear, which is returned to them if not sold.

The groups conducting the swap withhold 10% of the selling price. Sporting goods stores also set up booths to dispose of their merchandise at bargain prices. This is a great way for beginners to suit up. Dressing rooms are available. There is an admission charge to the public.

Flyers are sent to people who have attended previous shows, and the event is advertised by poster, magazine ads, and bumper stickers.

# Damaged Freight Outlets

(Also see **Part 1: General Merchandise-Liquidators**)

**M. JESSUP CO.**
3906 Adeline St., Emeryville 94608. Phone: 653-1522. Hours: M-Sat 8:30am-4:45pm. Purchases: BA MC. Parking: Street.

Other Store: 705 N. 13th St., San Jose.

The clutter at *M. Jessup* makes it hard to find what you want at first glance, but when you do it's like unearthing a treasure. It's almost impossible to leave this huge salvage store empty-handed. I stop in frequently because this is about the only salvage store that always has a good selection of name brand cosmetics of all types for 40% off the retail prices. These cosmetics are not outdated, just the result of freight or trucking company losses. In the last few years *M. Jessup* has been successful at buying up lines of giftware from the West Coast wholesale gift shows. Savings on prestige lines of gourmet cookware, crystal, copper, wooden trays and bowls and accessories are approximately 50% off. Food products, sundries, stationery, fabric, garden supplies, luggage, and clothing are also some of the types of merchandise always available at fantastic prices.

## LAZARUS SALES CO.
2133 Taraval, San Francisco. Phone: 661-9450. Hours: M-F, 12am-6pm, Sat 10am-6pm, Sun 12noon-5pm. Purchases: BA, MC. Parking: Street.

Other Store: **Furniture Annex,** 4117 Judah, San Francisco.

You can't help but wonder where they get all this "stuff" when you take a look around. Imagine anything sold in a department or variety store and you've about covered all the types of merchandise that are jammed into every nook and cranny. As a salvage dealer, the selection is rarely predictable, but you can always find at least one or two things worth buying. I stocked up on light bulbs at $1.00/pkg. of four on my last visit. The regular price is $2.28 at my local supermarket. Some outstanding buys can be made on furniture that was freight damaged but repaired then priced at approximately 40% below retail. The owners delight in telling you what was wrong with each piece, then describe with pride their professional repair work. There's more furniture at their Judah Street *Furniture Annex* that you'll want to peruse.

You may be lucky and find just what you want and what your pocketbook can afford.

## PAUL'S DEPARTMENT STORES
111 Calif. St., San Francisco. Phone: 391-8607. Hours: M-Sat, 8:30am-5pm. Purchases: BA, MC. Parking: Street, pay lots.

Other Stores: Sacramento, San Francisco (57 1st St., 2 Pine St.), South San Francisco.

You know that this is one of "those" places when you walk in the door and see all the people scrambling through jumbled displays of merchandise. Most of the goods in this store are acquired through factory overstocks or insurance writeoffs. New merchandise is always arriving; what's here today will be gone tomorrow. You are likely to find almost anything here; cosmetics, household needs, small appliances, goods for the handyman, and—best of all—really great buys on clothing. At first glance it's hard to believe that you could find anything good on these bulging racks—but you'll find closeouts, salesmen's samples, name-brand seconds, and irregulars at a fraction of retail prices. This is strictly a self-service store. Two curtained-off dressing rooms are barely adequate for the line of customers waiting their turn. Cash refunds are available on all but special sale merchandise.

# Flea Markets

Attending flea markets is getting to be a national weekend pastime. On any leisurely Saturday or Sunday, many families leave their all-too-peaceful homes to enjoy the harried, tumultuous bargaining and selling at a nearby swap meet or flea market. Absolutely everything imaginable is for sale, from post-World War II surplus wheelbarrows for $3 (the sturdy heavy-duty kind) to eggs, bakery, and produce so cheap it makes you wonder why everyone doesn't shop here instead of their local supermarket. Most flea markets require a hopeful seller to pay a fee to set up a booth. Sometimes prospective customers are also charged a token amount to park or to enter. The booths are arranged sometimes haphazardly, in a large fenced-in field or yard. Cheerful chaos is the order of the day. Items for sale are those that sellers have carried from their homes (like a portable garage sale) or have acquired through liquidating stores; some items are from closeouts or from auctions of surplus goods. Some people sell things at flea markets as a regular business, spending the days between weekends collecting stuff for the next sale. Prices are often a problem though, for most sellers are amateurs in the retailing business—sometimes they price too high, sometimes too low. Get into the swing of things—if you see something you want, make an offer (remembering that the seller is as anxious to sell as you are to buy). Haggling is part and parcel of the flea-market way of life.

It may take all day just to navigate through the crowds and see everything. Most clothing must be purchased without trying on, since few vendors have dressing rooms (a few with campers as their base of operations will allow you to wiggle and squeeze into your garments inside their vans). Most merchandise is sold "as is," and it's strictly "buyer beware." Most of the small appliance and home entertainment equipment booths give written guarantees and will make exchanges on defective merchandise if the proper receipt is presented. Most vendors operate on a cash-only basis; only a few accept credit cards.

Listed here are some of the better-known markets in the area; these are held regularly throughout the year. Other markets occur on some other basis—maybe monthly or annually. These smaller fairs can be fantastic sources of bargains by virtue of the fact that they are not as well traveled as the others. Check your local papers for notices of these events.

Also check out the unique "Flea Market and Collectors' Guide," a monthly circular that prints schedules of local collectors' shows, arts and crafts shows, and flea markets. For subscription information write P.O. Box 563, Mill Valley 94941.

## ALAMEDA PENNY MARKET
Island Auto Movie, 791 Thau Way (3 blocks south of the Alameda Tube), Alameda 94501. Phone: 522-7206. Hours: Sat, Sun 7am-4pm. Purchases: Cash only. Parking: Free.

*The Penny Market* at the Island Auto Movie Drive-In Theatre is a bargain hunter's paradise. Spaces are rented by the day, weekend, or month to anyone wishing to sell merchandise. Many vendors make a handsome living selling name-brand, first-quality stereo equipment, tapes, clothing, etc. in this low-overhead type of operation. Clothing, household goods, toys, and furniture (you name it) are available new and used.

## CASTRO VALLEY FLEA MARKET
20820 Oak St. (at Castro Valley Blvd.), Castro Valley. Phone: 582-0396. Hours: Sat, Sun 7am-5pm. Purchases: Cash only. Parking: Free.

Admission is free.

## HILLTOP DRIVE-IN FLEA MARKET
Hilltop Dr. & Hwy. 80, Richmond 94804. Phone: 467-4849 for information. Hours: Sun 7am-4pm. Purchases: Cash only. Parking: Free.

On Sundays a modest 50¢ is charged per car. There are approximately 150 booths with new and used general merchandise. (All potential sellers must first fill out a police report describing their wares and leave proof of their identification such as driver's license, which prevents the sale of stolen merchandise.)

## SAN FRANCISCO FLEA MARKET
601 Tunnel Ave., San Francisco 94134. Phone: 467-4849. Hours: Sat, Sun 7am-5pm. Purchases: Cash only. Parking: Free lot.

Admission is 25¢ per person.

## SAN JOSE FLEA MARKET
12000 Berryessa Rd., San Jose 95133. Phone: 297-3346. Hours: Sat, Sun 7:30am-sundown. Purchases: Cash only. Parking: Pay lot.

Admission is free.

## SANTA CLARA FLEA MARKET
5500 Lafayette St. (Mountain View-Alviso Rd., Route 237). Santa Clara 95050. Phone 988-0850. Hours: Sat, Sun 7am-6pm. Purchases: Cash only. Parking: Free lot.

Nonprofit organizations sell free here. Sellers pay $3 for Saturday and stay free on Sunday. Buyers in free on Saturday until 11 am.

## SOLANO DRIVE-IN FLEA MARKET
Solano Way & Hwy. 4, Concord 94521. Phone: 467-4849 for information. Hours: Sat, Sun 7am-4pm. Purchases: Cash only. Parking:Free.

On Saturday admission is free; on Sunday it is 50¢ per car. There are approximately 200 booths selling new and used general merchandise.

# Garage Sales and Shopping Circulars

A weekend spent hopping from garage sale to garage sale is getting to be a leisure-time activity for folks rich and poor, famous and not so famous. Garage sales, like flea markets, are a favorite American weekend pastime. They're held by private parties, either one family or several, who clean out their garages and homes to make money on obsolete, outdated, miscellaneous trivia. You can find lots of great items; other people's junk may be your treasure! And the snazzier the neighborhood the snazzier the junk. We've even heard of Hillsborough trash retrievers doing very well.

You can get some great bargains from private sales, usually advertised in newspapers servicing the smaller communities. Once you become accustomed to looking through the local newspapers, you'll discover that many businesses advertise their best bargains in the classified sections, too. The goods you can buy this way range from new through slightly to very used. There's a technique to looking through newspapers for bargains. Be sure to use the index, which conveniently organizes all the ads. Having an idea of what you need or want helps when you check through classifications like Announcements, Auctions, Mail Order, Flea Markets, Garage Sales, and Merchandise for Sale. This last section is sometimes further arranged in listings for antiques, appliances, cameras equipment, household goods, and that wonderful catch-all "Miscellaneous for Sale." Many people hesitate to shop through newspaper ads, and admittedly, it can be confusing. But there is a method that helps eliminate a bit of it. Take a pen and find a classification that seems as if it might have the item you're looking for. Reading down the column, draw a continuous vertical line through those ads that don't have what you want; circle those that look like a good prospect. Skip over the ads that are too nebulous (those that say "household goods for sale" or "moving sale" and nothing else). Unless you're looking for lots of miscellaneous stuff, these can be a waste of your time. You want those with a short description of some of the larger items for sale, including a phone number.

There are several small weekly or monthly newspapers available in the Bay Area which offer only good news for the bargain shopper, since they have only one section—the want ads. Both regular retailers and private parties advertise in these papers. You can see almost everything for sale here—appliances, boats, bikes, tools, furniture, antiques. Some of the papers suggest that advertisers list items for at least 50% less than regular retail. These papers have wide circulation—most of them are free and can be picked up at your local grocer's. If you need to sell something, a few of the papers have an "advertise free—pay when you sell" policy, a way for you to save money too.

Once you have selected several good ads, get out a map and pinpoint the places, which eliminates backtracking when you are on your way. If you see something you like and want, buy it while you can—someone right behind you might take it without

Also, remember that a bargain is not a bargain unless you need or really want it. Garage sale shopping is hard on the psyche, because sometimes it's hard to pass up a perfectly good blender or waffle iron or coffee grinder for only $1 even though you still have two at home that you got as wedding gifts.

The best times to check newspapers are Thursdays, Fridays, Saturdays, and of course, Sunday mornings. Be sure to check the following: Contra Costa "Times" (East Bay area); Hayward "Tribune"; Palo Alto "Times"; Redwood City "Tribune"; San Francisco "Progress"; San Jose "Mercury"; San Mateo "Times."

# Resale Shops

Here's your chance to have finer clothes at prices you can afford. A resale shop is the "top drawer" of the used clothing business. Usually their prices are higher than thrift shops. The affluent (who really do wear their clothes only a few times and then discard them use these shops as a moneymaking outlet for disposing of their apparel. Most of the resale shops operate on a consignment basis. It works this way: the potential seller brings in any items she wants to dispose of, and the store agrees to try to sell the items for her for a certain percentage of the price. Other stores agree on the price the item will go for (the amount depending on item's condition and age), and this is split fifty-fifty with the shop owner. Other shops buy outright. On this kind of a deal, everyone makes some money: the socialite makes a profit, the store owner makes a profit, and you the

customer, make good buys on clothing you couldn't otherwise afford. You will be saving 50-70% buying this way; when you pay $40 for a dress, it probably cost about $200 new. You'll find some very sophisticated clothes with designer labels like Givenchy, Oscar de la Renta, and Donald Brooks, as well as labels from local finer department and specialty stores. It is impossible to list all the many better resale shops which abound in the Bay Area. Your best resource is the yellow pages of the phone book. Check listings under "Clothing: Used." I have always found that the Junior Leagues' Next to New Shops in San Francisco and Oakland to be excellent for quality of merchandise and selection. The Heritage House at 3333 Mt. Diablo Blvd., Lafayette is—hands down—the best consignment shop in Contra Costa County.

# Surplus Stores

**AAA EQUIPMENT**
745 50th Ave., Oakland 94601. Phone: 261-2443. Hours: M-F 8am-4:30pm; Sat 8am-3pm. Purchases: Cash, check. Parking: Street.

A sign "For Men Only" would seem appropriate on the outside of this business, located on three acres near the Nimitz Freeway in Oakland. A stack of "Playboy" magazines in the office is for the diversion of the customers waiting for service; another sign in the office boasts "We Talk Hardhat Here." It behooves you to avoid shopping on rainy days, since most of the merchandise is displayed outdoors. You can buy everything here from small hand tools (new and used) to huge pieces of construction equipment. Contractors, firms, and handymen come to AAA to avail themselves of the tremendous selection of government surplus and bankrupt stock. Savings of 50% are not unusual on used machinery like air compressors, generators, portable power plants, roller conveyors, and stainless steel items.

This is the place to shop for concrete trucks, crawler tractors, yard cranes, or fork lifts. The yard man will direct you through the maze of equipment to your special need and will gladly test the equipment for you. Anyone contemplating a purchase is free to bring in outside experts to appraise and evaluate the equipment. All equipment and machinery is in working order when sold. Although no guarantees are given, AAA tries to stand behind its merchandise.

## BONANZA WHOLESALE DISTRIBUTORS

3617 E. 14th St., Oakland 94601. Phone: 534-3030. Hours: M-F 8:30-5:30pm, Sat 8am-5pm. Purchases: BA, MC. Parking: Street.

This is a gadgeteer's paradise. A friend tells me he comes here when he can't find what he's looking for anywhere else. There are tons of tools, hardware, bolts, tape, cable, chain, compressors, motors, wheels, plumbing supplies, and on and on. You'll probably have to ask for assistance to locate your particular item amid the organized chaos that prevails. I did notice that all nails, screws, and bolts were neatly arranged in boxes according to size, and I was told that a reorganization is under way to label all those cluttered aisles.

All new electrical motors are given a 90-day guarantee; used motors carry a 30-day guarantee and are tested for you in the store. Prices are lower than those of your neighborhood hardware store, since most merchandise comes from government or industrial surplus or from stores going out of business. Special shipments are advertised in the classified section of the Oakland "Tribune."

## J&H OUTLET

476 Industrial Way, San Carlos 94070. Phone: 591-7113. Hours: M-F 10am-6pm, Sat 10am-3pm. Purchases: Cash, check, Parking: Street.

J&H Outlet is tailor-made for all you tinkerers with components and audio equipment. It consists of a cavernous room filled with practically everything you could possibly need at low, low prices. There are literally millions of surplus items—thousands of components, lots of wires, all kinds of parts, and very good buys on copper and brass remnants for jewelrymakers and sculptors. Mr. Ingethron, owner of J&H, is helpful and nice. He and his staff are willing to help you find what you need or get it for you if they possibly can.

UNITED SURPLUS SALES
(See **Part I: Arts, Crafts, Hobby Supplies**)

# Thrift Shops

Moving, remodeling, marriage, divorce, and death all contribute to the unearthing of items no longer needed but too good to throw away. At least half of the "too good to throw away" items end up being donated to charitable organizations which redistribute them through thrift shops. The donations come from many sources; sometimes a will leaves an entire estate to an organization, or a large corporation redoing its offices will simply hand its old stuff to a thrift shop for a tax deduction rather than incur the headache and expense of moving. Of course, there are also those who are simply cleaning out their attic, closet, or basement and call their favorite thrift shop to remove the discards. Whatever the reason, many valuable antiques and collectables with obscure histories often end up here; for the "pro" bargain hunter thrift shops are a must. These places are also becoming more and more "in" for the decorators and collectors (which ought to tell you something). Most larger thrift stores operate on a similar basis, with the same store policies on exchanges, returns, etc. Most of them have everything priced clearly and arranged neatly for your perusal. We suggest checking out your local smaller thrift shop from time to time, too; smaller stores are often less picked over than the larger ones. We've not listed three good old standbys—*Goodwill Industries, Salvation Army,* and the *St. Vincent de Paul Society.* All offer great bargains and there are many located throughout the Bay Area. Check the white pages of your phone book.

# Wrecking and Salvage Yards

**CHAS. S. CAMPANELLA WRECKING**
2700 E. 7th St., Oakland 94601. Phone: 536-7002. Hours: M-Sat 8am-5pm. Purchases: BA, MC. Parking: Street.

Other yard: 5401 San Leandro Blvd., Oakland

If you're trying to achieve that "funky" look in your decorating or if you're just leery of putting new wood on top of old wood, try browsing through the assortment of old doors, windows, and artifacts often available at this wrecking yard. Campanella frequently demolishes old Victorian houses, amassing an assortment of newel posts, footed bathtubs, wooden columns, or windows (curved or straight, made of leaded, stained, or beveled glass), and the like. You'll be saving 50-70% off the cost of new doors or windows, and all you have to do is measure the doors and windows for yourself when making your choice.

There is also a big selection of used plywood, large beams (good for sub-flooring), used brick, concrete foundation blocks, and many other types of used building materials—great dollar savers for a thrifty remodeling job or even new construction. Occasionally they run ads in the Oakland "Tribune" when an interesting inventory is acquired through a wrecking job. You may call in advance and get information about forthcoming jobs, where you might buy directly at the site for even greater savings.

**CLEVELAND WRECKING COMPANY**
2800 3rd St., San Francisco 94107. Phone: 824-1411. Hours: M-F 8am-5pm; Sat 8am-1pm. Purchases: BA, MC. Parking: Street, free lot.

Much of what the San Francisco branch of this large wrecking company demolished is for sale in their yard. Any kind of building material you may need—used plywood, paneling, lumber, doors, windows and glass, electrical or plumbing equipment—is for sale here for a fraction of its original price. The stock changes constantly, depending on the building currently being demolished.

You can save even more when you buy the materials directly at the demolition site. You can learn about site sales by calling the office or by checking the San Francisco "Chronicle" under "Announcements." Know your measurements before you buy; there are no returns without the original sales slip and they charge for all merchandise returned (on new material, 10% of the cost; on used material, 20%). All new items for sale (lumber, heaters, roofing materials) go for discount prices.

You can find some really arty stuff here if you take your time and don't mind venturing into their big yard in back of the main building.

# Alphabetical Index

# Geographical Index

# Subject Index

# Additions and New Listings

## Additions

Page 90—**Wherehouse for Bedspreads:** New store is in Menlo Park at 935 El Camino Real. Phone: 322-6224.

Page 108—**M. Jessup Co.:** New stores are in Antioch at 611 3rd St.; in Pleasant Hill at 2665 Pleasant Hill Rd. (at Taylor Blvd.), phone: 935-1640; and in San Mateo at 101 "B" St.

## New Listings

## Clothing

**BETWEEN THE BUTTONS**
524 3rd St., San Francisco 94103. Phone: 543-0354. Hours: M-Sat Noon-5pm. Purchases: BA, MC, VISA. Parking: Street.

Sticky Fingers makes Unisex jeans which are very popular with the fashion minded younger set. This outlet is the last post outlet for their seconds at approximately 50% off retail prices. If you're very tall or very short you may find their make-shift dressing rooms with short curtains reveal more of you than you'd like. Check the merchandise carefully, there are no exchanges. The size range in waist sizes is 25-36.

## DESIGNER'S OUTLET
1357 No. Main Street, Walnut Creek 94596. Phone : 932-1728. Hours: M-F 10am-9pm, Sat 10am-6pm, Sun 11am-6pm. Purchases: MC, VISA. Parking: Street.

Other Store: 951 Contra Costa Blvd., Pleasant Hill.

The V.I.P. card presented to you with your initial purchase entitles the buyer an additional 15% saving on the next purchase within 30 days. A nice extra, considering that prices are already discounted 30-50% off retail prices. Junior sizes 3-13 and Misses sizes 8-20 provide a well rounded selection for women 16 to 60. There is a nice emphasis given to the fashion needs of the mature women who likes a sophisticated look. Most lines are over-runs from New York and Los Angeles manufacturers'.

## FASHIONS UNLIMITED
5100-5 Clayton Road (Vineyard Shopping Center), Concord 94521. Phone: 835-3874. Hours: M-F 9:30am-9pm, Sat 9am-6pm, Sun 11am-5pm. Purchases: BA, MC, VISA. Parking: Free lot.

Bobbi Brooks, Garland, Huck-A-Poo, Modern Juniors, Villager and Larry Levine are just a few of the prominent manufacturers represented in the selection of Juniors and Misses clothing at this new 4,000 sq. ft. store. All the labels are left intact on this first quality merchandise which includes dresses, separates, blazers, raincoats, and ski clothing.

The greatest strength of this store is the selection of clothing from manufacturers throughout the country, which offers shoppers a refreshing choice in making their purchases. Careful buying enables the owners to pass on savings of 30-60% off retail prices. Dressing rooms, exchange privileges, and a sparkling fresh decor should spell success for the owners and their value-conscious customers.

## LADIES' TENNIS OUTLET
1070 Shary Circle, Concord. Phone: 825-4470. Hours: FRIDAY's ONLY 10am-4pm. Purchases: Cash, Check. Parking: Street.

Many samples, factory over-runs and some irregulars in S-M-L sizes make up the selection of ladies' tennis dresses, shorts, T-shirts, and cover-ups. The factory store, located in an industrial park off Detroit Avenue, is only open on Friday's. Great selection! Terrific prices!

## OAKLAND MANUFACTURER'S OUTLET
320 10th Street, Oakland. Phone: 893-9290. Hours: Tues-Sat 10am-4pm. Purchases: BA, MC. Parking: Street.

Clothes designed for the price conscious younger woman (18-35 yrs.) constitutes the selection of related separates manufactured by this Oakland company. Prices ($7.-$13.) at the outlet are approximately 40-50% off retail on the over-runs sent down from the factory upstairs. Size range is 3-13.

### SHAZAM
254 Clement St., San Francisco, Phone: 221-2854. Hours: M-Sat 10am-6pm. Purchases: BA, MC. Parking: Street.

The ambiance of this store is right out of a disco dance club, complete with flashing lights and vibrating background music. Savings of 15-30% are possible on the chic collection of the latest fashions for the younger fashion-minded woman. Dresses and separates in Jr. sizes will help you create that "foxy look", perfect for weekend happenings.

# Fabrics

### FABRIC WAREHOUSE
2327 McKee Road, San Jose 95116. Phone: 926-3203. Hours: M-F 10am-9pm, Sat 10am-6pm, Sun Noon-5pm. Purchases: BA, MC, VISA. Parking: Free lot.

Other Stores: 3690 El Camino Real, Santa Clara; 898 Blossom Hill Road, San Jose.

Picture a supermarket-sized store filled with fabrics and you can understand how overwhelmed you'll feel on your first visit to these warehouse stores, located next to K-Mart. Most of these fabrics are purchased directly from Eastern mills, and all are first quality. Except for wools, their selection is very extensive in all categories.

Prices on upholstery and drapery fabrics are low enough to lure upholsterers into the store to buy fabrics for their customers; they're often 50-60% off retail. Everyday regular prices reflect savings of 20-25% off established retail prices on all their goods, greater reductions are on fabrics advertised in their special weekly promotions.

They have an interesting dual pricing policy based on full bolt purchases vs. cut to order. The full bolt lower price refers to any amount of yardage remaining on a bolt, whether it's 3 yds. or 40 yds. All notions are discounted 15-20% off manufacturer's list price and all patterns are discounted 15%.

# Linens

### DECORATOR'S BEDSPREAD OUTLET
5757 Pacheco Blvd (1 mile north of Sun Valley Mall), Pacheco 94553. Phone: 689-3435. Hours: M-Sat 9:30am-5:30pm, Fri 9:30am-9pm, Sun Noon-5pm. Purchases: BA, MC, VISA. Parking: Lot.

It's so nice to find a store owner who is able and willing to operate a business with a lower overhead, take a smaller mark-up, and pass on savings to consumers. It helps to have good connections, too. The selection of bedspreads, comforters, decorator pillows, dust ruffles and towels has the depth and variety to suit the taste and requirements of just about everyone.

Savings on regular, first quality merchandise (the same merchandise you see in better stores) is approximately 25% below prevailing retail. On custom orders you can save 15%. The best buys are on special purchase items—overcuts, cancellations, or discounted merchandise from manufacturers—that result in savings of 40-70%. The price range in their selection is very accommodating. There are budget priced goods for lean budgets, and higher prices for fine quality custom-type spreads. The goods are neatly displayed and there are several "mock beds", useful for seeing your spread in a home situation. They also have a reasonable trial purchase policy, which allows you to take the merchandise home on approval. Low prices, good service . . . what more could you ask for?

# Toys

### TOY PUPPET OUTLET
5705 Hollis (corner Powell & Hollis), Emeryville 94608. Phone: 658-7677. Hours: M-F 10am-4pm. Purchases: BA, MC. Parking: Street.

These very expensive furry puppet animals have become very popular with specialty toy shops because of their unique and appealing life-like appearance. Otters, oppossums, skunks, foxes, etc. look like the real animals and are a far cry from the typical puppet. In fact, they don't look like puppets at all, but more like stuffed animals. The prices on their selection of seconds with minor flaws are about 50% off retail.

# Dinnerware and Accessories

## Restaurant Supply Store

### ROYAL SUPPLY CO.
501 15th Street (Corner San Bruno), San Francisco. Phone: 626-1700. Hours: M-F 8:30am-5pm. Purchases: Cash, Check.

The closeout room of this major distributor is a bonanza for anyone shopping for good quality, glasses, barware, stemware or sturdy restaurant china at super low prices. These items can be purchased in any quantity from the closeout room. At these prices I couldn't resist a dozen Bloody Mary or Ice Tea glasses at $2.10 and with a few extra I don't have to worry about breakage. Many of these glasses would make lovely gifts. Your bargain gift will make you look positively magnanimous!